DEVELOPING SHAPE, SPACE & MEASURES WITH 7-9 YEAR OLDS

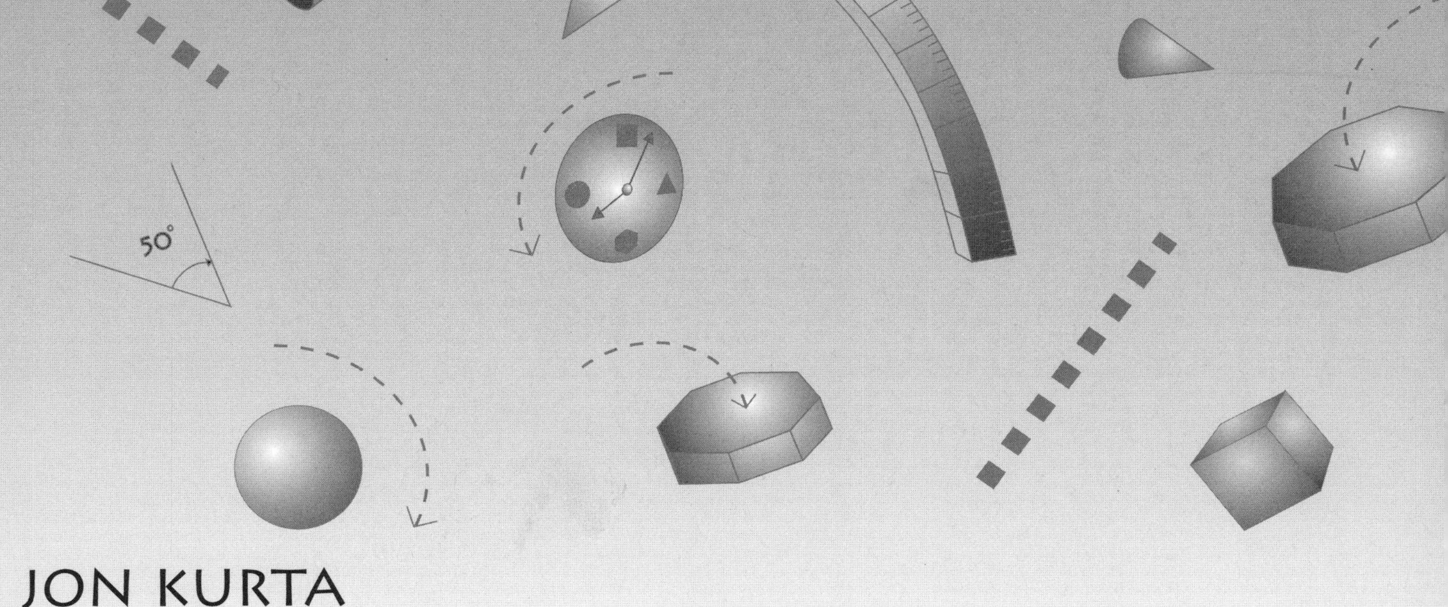

JON KURTA

Published by Scholastic Ltd
Villiers House
Clarendon Avenue
Leamington Spa
Warwickshire CV32 5PR

1 2 3 4 5 6 7 8 9 0   0 1 2 3 4 5 6 7 8 9

AUTHOR
Jon Kurta

SERIES CONSULTANT
Jon Kurta

EDITOR
Joel Lane

ASSISTANT EDITORS
Marian Reeve and David Sandford

SERIES DESIGNERS
Anna Oliwa and Sarah Rock

DESIGNER
Paul Cheshire

ILLUSTRATIONS
Duncan Scott

COVER ARTWORK
Mark Oliver at Illustration

Designed using Adobe Pagemaker

British Library Cataloguing-in-Publication Data
A catalogue record for this book is available from the British Library.

ISBN 0-439-01774-2

CONTENTS

ABOUT THE AUTHOR

Jon Kurta is a lecturer in mathematics ITT at Surrey University, Roehampton. He has written several successful mathematics titles for Scholastic, including *Developing Mental Maths with 7–9 year olds*, *Practising Mental Maths with 8–11 year olds* and *Resource Bank: Handling Data*.

This book is dedicated to my colleagues in the Maths team at Roehampton.

When asked what constitutes the content of mathematics in the primary school, many people will think solely of arithmetical calculation. This part of the curriculum has been emphasized in the contemporary concern with standards that has led to the development of the *National Numeracy Strategy: Framework for Teaching Mathematics* (March 1999) and the introduction of the 'daily mathematics lesson'. However, it is interesting that in the international studies that provoked such concern (such as the TIMMS study), British children actually performed well in comparison to their peers in spatial topics. This perhaps reflects the strong tradition in British primary schools of work on shape, space and measures – a tradition that embraces the Montessori philosophy, as well as Piagetian notions of 'learning through experience', and which has often involved the innovative use of a range of practical materials (geoboards, geostrips, Poleidoblocs and others).

In children's everyday experiences, spatial encounters precede numerical ones. In the pre-school years, children are curious about their environment and keen to become familiar with the look and feel of everything around them. A young child picking up and pulling objects could be estimating their size and weight, as well as exploring the relationship between these attributes. As they learn to speak, children develop appropriate language to help them articulate their developing spatial awareness. Taken a step further, we can see how spatial awareness is as important as numerical awareness in many professions – for example, building, carpentry and engineering.

This book provides activities that acknowledge sound practice in the teaching of shape, space and measures, but also aim to embrace contemporary issues. Particular emphasis is given to visualizing aspects of the topics, and to the role of language – both in the sense of accurate use and understanding of 'technical' vocabulary and in the sense of being aware of talk and discussion as an important mode of learning.

SHAPE AND SPACE

DEVELOPING VOCABULARY

SCAA's review of the 1996 Key Stage 2 SATs suggested that teachers needed to place more emphasis on the use of correct mathematical vocabulary for geometric shapes. It is not uncommon to hear children (and adults) referring to a ball as 'circle-shaped' and a box as 'square'. This misconception needs to be addressed, not glossed over. Typical misconceptions that occur in this area are well documented in the OFSTED Research Report*, and many are addressed directly in activities in this book. For example, research shows that children are less likely to recognize and name correctly shapes that are shown obliquely or that are irregular.

WORKING MENTALLY

The difficulties outlined also highlight the importance of talk and discussion. I may know what 'parallel lines' means, and I can close my eyes and picture them, but without dialogue it is unclear whether a group of children have the same mental picture. Spatial activities clearly need to involve a mental element as well as a physical one, and the ability to visualize objects spatially is important in everyday adult life.

It can also be argued that visualizing in spatial activities will be useful for children's development in mental calculation. For example, realizing that the subtraction 82 – 78 is best done by adding on from 78 may be helped by picturing the position of the numbers on a number line. Other examples include 'knowing' and using the dot patterns on a dice to recognize numbers and understanding how multiplication can be modelled with 'arrays' that link directly to area:

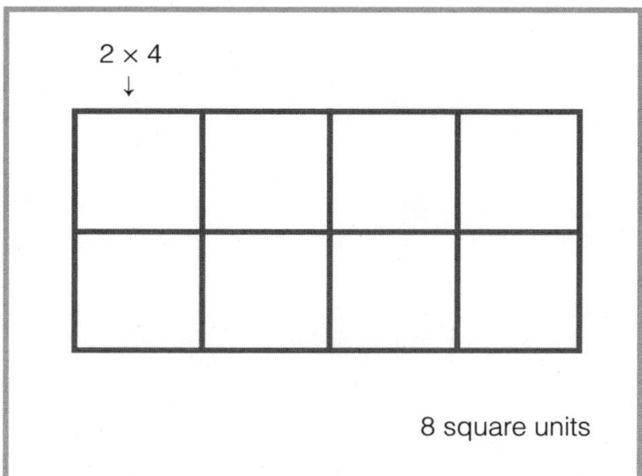

In the development of algebraic thinking, the use of patterns that combine a spatial element with a numerical element is also common practice. For example, the 'growing L' image is a visual way of representing odd numbers:

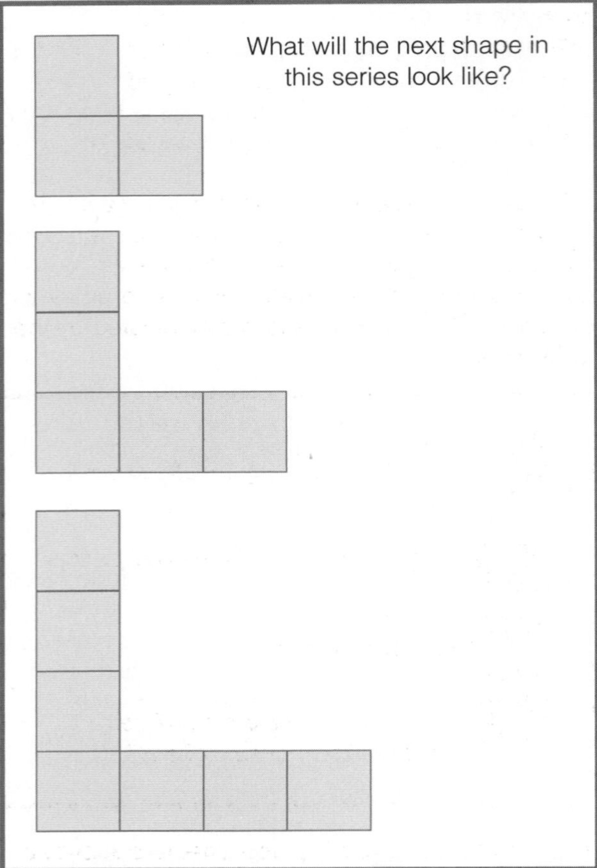

What will the next shape in this series look like?

MEASURES

Work on measures in primary schools is often seen primarily as a context for developing number. This can be seen both in word problems involving use of the four operations (often at the end of a page of 'pure' calculations) and in the use of metric measures to contextualize work on place value and decimals. While not ignoring this aspect, this book puts particular emphasis on conceptual understanding of measures. As with shape and space, there is an emphasis on visualization and discussion. (Further activities on calculations with measure can be found in the companion Scholastic series *Developing Mental Maths* and *Practising Mental Maths*.)

It is important that the teaching of measures should include:

- ***Developing a 'feel' for what is being measured and the right words to express it.*** *This involves firstly linking known words to the appropriate measure (for example,* ***heavy*** *and* ***light*** *are related to weight,* ***full*** *and* ***empty*** *to capacity), and secondly having a sense of the relative sizes of different objects – Which is the heavier stone? Which cup holds the most?*

- ***Being able to make 'common sense' estimates.*** *In many real-life practical situations involving quantities, we do not need to know an exact measure: for example, when parking my car, putting milk in my coffee or buying a handful of vegetables, I only have an approximate idea of the length of available kerb, the volume of milk or the weight of the vegetables respectively. However, I am confident that I won't hit the car behind, overfill my cup of coffee or buy too many vegetables. It is important to help children build up this 'common sense' of different measures.*

- ***Systems of units.*** *Children need to know both the numerical relationships between units (such as 100cm = 1m) and their relative magnitude in practical use. For example, the length of a pencil is best measured in centimetres, but the distance across the playground is best measured in metres. It is important to build up children's images of the relative size of different units.*

SOLVING PROBLEMS

While learning about shape, space and measures, children need to be actively engaged in problem solving. This provides a purposeful context for the development of skills and an environment that fosters discussion. Talk needs to be skilfully led in order to make sure the children's attention is focused and misconceptions are addressed. It also provides a vehicle for assessment of the children's understanding.

Additionally, it is through talk that a shared understanding of particular vocabulary can be established. For example, the concept of the conservation of area can be built up by talking about how a surface can be covered with cubes or squared paper, then how the cubes or pieces of the squared paper can be rearranged.

ABOUT THIS BOOK

This book is split into two main sections: 'Shape and space' and 'Measures'. Each section starts with a double-page glossary (pages 8–9 and 76–77) which highlights relevant vocabulary, particularly where it is likely to be new to this age group. Each glossary can be enlarged for display as an A2 poster (copy each A4 page separately onto A3, then join them back together) or copied at normal size for desktop use.

The two main sections are divided into sub-sections dealing with particular topics. Each sub-section starts with a two-page spread, highlighting:

- ***Key ideas.*** *What the children need to know overall – the key concepts that need to be considered when planning a unit of work on this topic for the appropriate age group.*

- ***Common misconceptions and difficulties.*** *Key teaching points, many of which are emphasized in particular activities.*

- ***What children should know by the end of Year 3/Primary 4 and Year 4/Primary 5.*** *This relates directly to the NNS* Framework for Teaching Mathematics*, the National Curriculum for England and Wales and the Scottish Guidelines for Maths 5–14.*

The activities presented in each sub-section fall into two categories: teacher-directed activities and group problem-solving. If you are following the National Numeracy Strategy, this division is well suited to the structure of the daily mathematics lesson.

The teacher-directed activities include ideas for introducing particular themes into whole-class discussion, including key questions which can be used for assessment. Some of these activities are short 'warm-ups' to use in the first part of the mathematics lesson; others are suitable for extended discussion in a plenary session following group work on the theme.

The group problem-solving activities are intended to involve the children in group work, and include suggestions for different ability groups (though, as with number activities, this may not always be necessary).

Supporting photocopiable sheets provide either practice activities or resources. The practice activity sheets are designed to consolidate the main concepts. They also stimulate personal reflection or discussion by asking questions as indicated by the following icons:

 *think (and be ready to talk) about it!*

 *discuss with your 'maths talk' partner*

 *tell your teacher*

 *write down [to help the children organize their ideas logically].*

The use of these photocopiable sheets is intended to be flexible. A class can be split, with half doing a practical activity and the other half working on a practice sheet. The sheets can be used after the completion of practical activities; some may also be useful for homework or individual assessment.

A photocopiable writing frame is provided on page 128. This will help the children to reflect on their learning, and could be particularly useful when they have been engaged in practical or investigative work that has not left much recorded evidence. Activities for which the writing frame is particularly helpful are highlighted in the teachers' notes. The writing frame can be used directly as it is; alternatively, when the children have developed confidence in their writing about maths, they could use it as a basis for a freer account of their work. Asking children to write about maths is a good way to find out how confident they are in their grasp of mathematical vocabulary, and also how able they are to communicate their ideas – two aspects of mathematics which are important themes in this book.

---

*Askew, M. and Wiliam, D. (1995) *Recent Research in Mathematics Education* London: HMSO.

Triangles **have three sides.**

- **Equilateral triangles** have three equal sides.

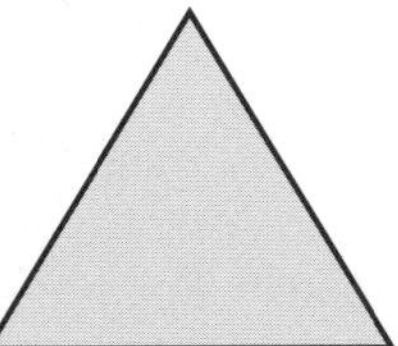

- **Isosceles triangles** have two equal sides.

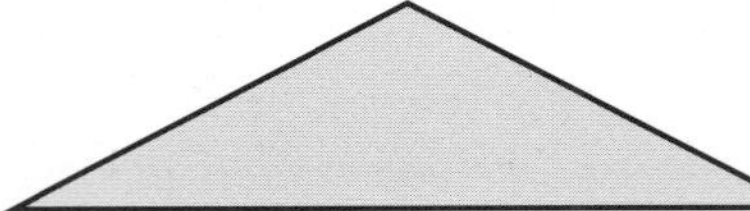

Quadrilaterals **have four sides.**

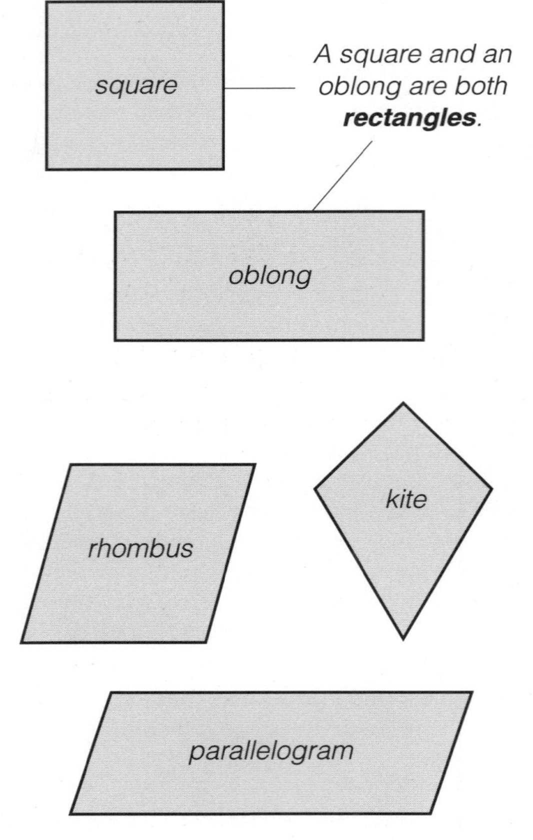

More than four sides

- **Pentagons** have five sides.
- **Hexagons** have six sides.

Regular and irregular

- Some shapes are **regular**: all their sides and angles are equal.
- Some are **irregular**: their sides and angles are not all the same.

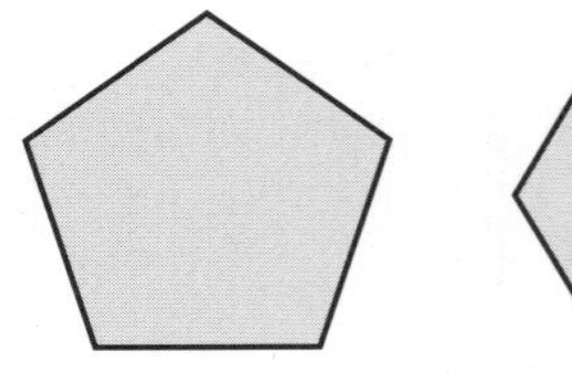

*These shapes are **regular**.*

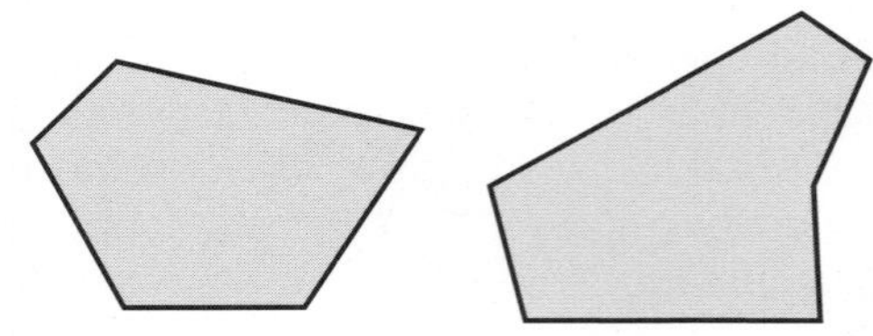

*These shapes are **irregular**.*

Convex and concave

- Most 2-D shapes are **convex**: all their corners point outwards...
- but some are **concave** and have one or more corners pointing in.

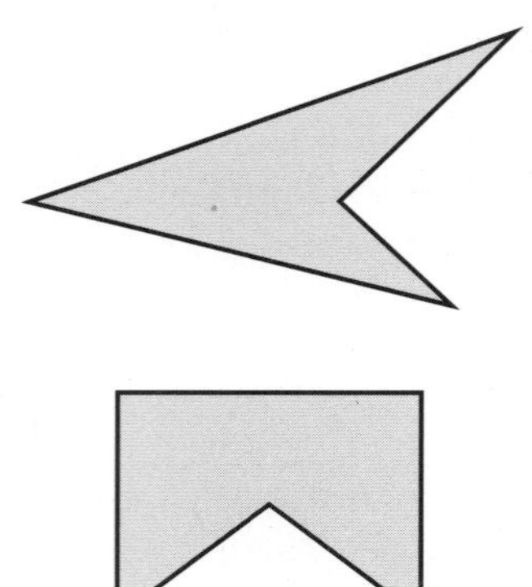

concave shapes

3-D SHAPES (POLYHEDRONS)

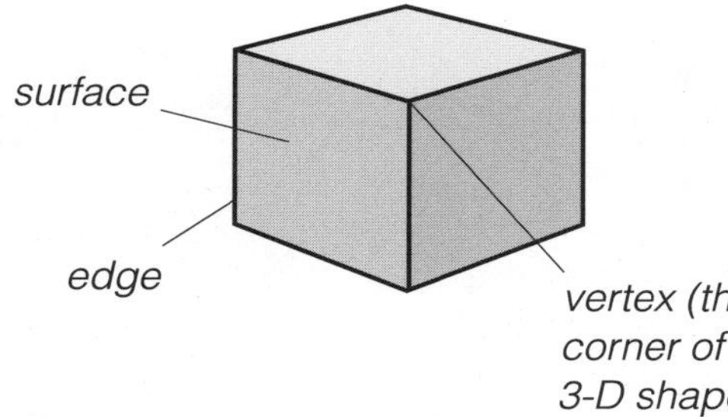

Prisms

Prisms have the same size of cross-section at any point along their length.

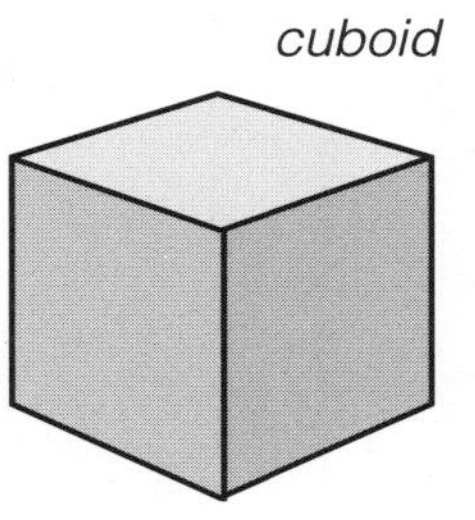
cuboid

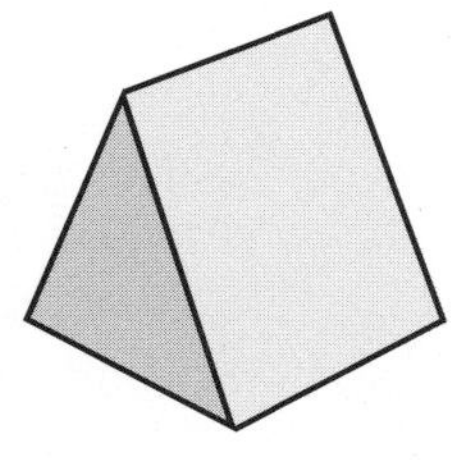
triangular prism

Pyramids

Pyramids are 3-D shapes that come to a point.

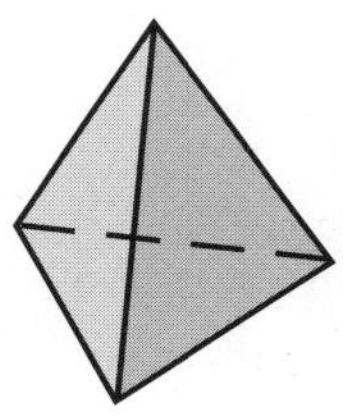
tetrahedron

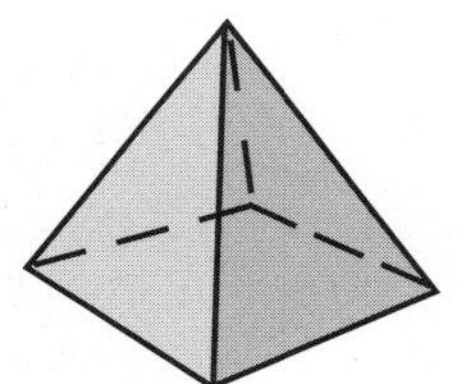
square-based pyramid

Other common 3-D shapes:

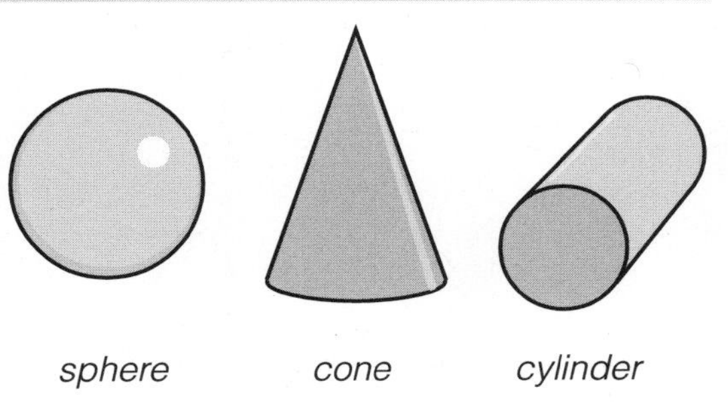

LINES & ANGLES

Lines

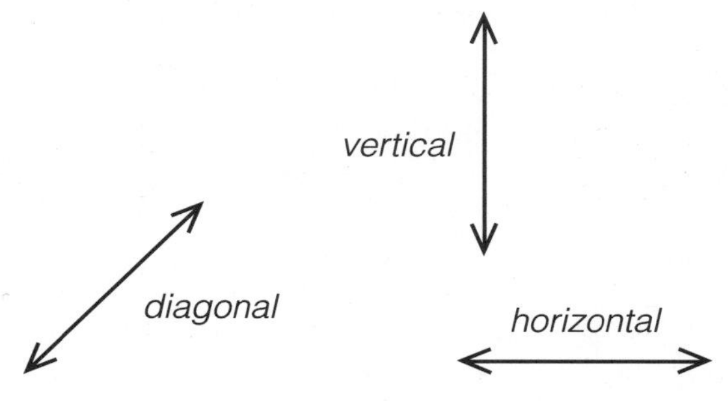

Symmetry

Some shapes have one or more **lines of symmetry**. These are lines that divide the shape into two halves that are **mirror images** of each other.

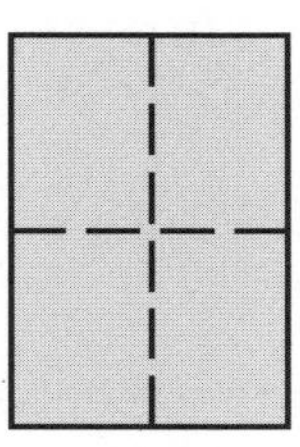

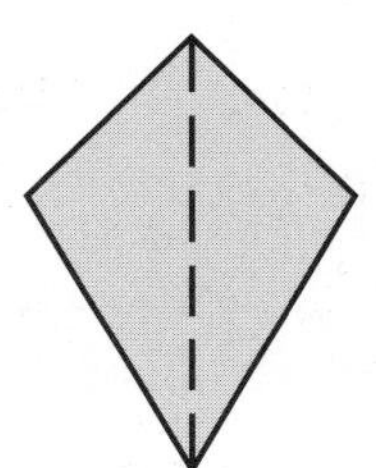

Angles

- **Angles** occur where two lines meet. The angle is the amount of **turn** between one line and the other.
- A **right angle** is a special angle that can be found in any corner of a rectangle (square or oblong).

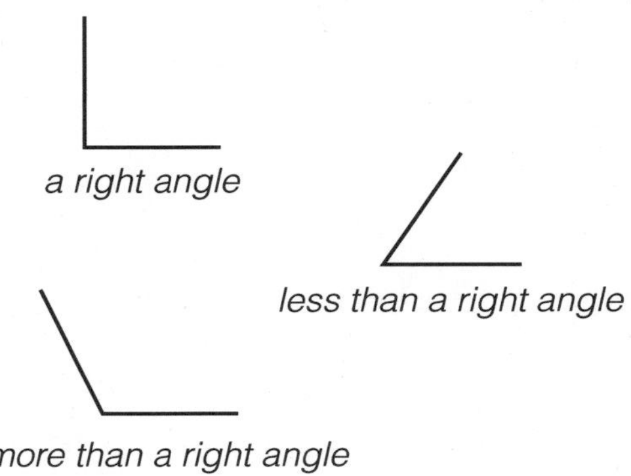

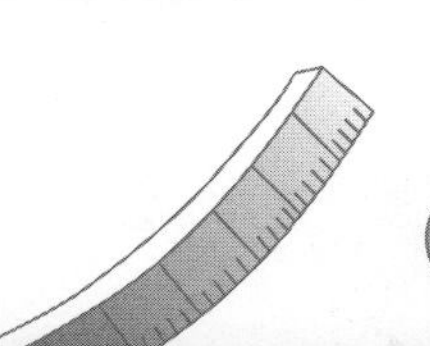

KEY IDEAS

- Using an increasing range of vocabulary (see Glossary for examples).
- Describing and classifying 3-D and 2-D shapes according to a range of properties.
- Understanding the relationship between 3-D and 2-D shapes.
- Visualizing shapes.
- Investigating statements about shapes.
- Making models, shapes and patterns using a variety of media and resources.

Between the ages of seven and nine, children are developing their conceptual understanding of the properties of different shapes. They are beginning to realize that shapes can be classified by a range of criteria: number of sides, type of angle, various types of symmetry and so on. They should be recognizing 'families of shapes' such as quadrilaterals, and be aware that not all four-sided shapes are rectangles (squares or oblongs). They may still be using informal vocabulary some of the time, but the appropriate geometrical language should be introduced and constantly reinforced. A difficulty here is that much of the mathematical vocabulary is not widely used outside of shape and space lessons; a wall dictionary (which the class can create together) is helpful in reinforcing this vocabulary. The Glossary on pages 8–9 could form the basis of such a dictionary.

Children should be exploring the properties of shapes using various types of practical equipment (such as geoboards, geostrips, Polydron and tangram sets) to make models, patterns and tessellations – practical experiences are vital for children's development. Just as important is the need to challenge children through appropriate questioning about shape properties, and to engage them in visualizing and reasoning activities. It is important to consider not only what a triangle is, but what shapes are **not** triangles – hence the use of Venn and Carroll diagrams for sorting.

BY THE END OF Y3/P4, MOST CHILDREN SHOULD BE ABLE TO:

- classify and describe 3-D and 2-D shapes, including the hemisphere, prism, semi-circle, quadrilateral
- refer to a range of properties (symmetry, number of sides, angles) in classifying shapes
- make and describe shapes and patterns (including making templates, and combining shapes to make more complex shapes)
- relate solid shapes to pictures of them
- investigate a general statement about familiar shapes by finding examples that satisfy it.

BY THE END OF Y4/P5, MOST CHILDREN SHOULD BE ABLE TO:

- classify and describe 3-D and 2-D shapes, including regular and irregular polygons and polyhedra (such as the heptagon and tetrahedron)
- classify polygons using criteria such as number of right angles, whether or not they are regular, symmetry properties
- make polygons using paper-folding or a pinboard
- draw circles using a variety of methods, recognizing the terms **radius** and **diameter**
- visualize 3-D shapes from 2-D drawings and identify simple nets of solid shapes
- make and investigate a general statement about familiar shapes by finding examples that satisfy it.

SOME COMMON MISCONCEPTIONS AND STRATEGIES TO CORRECT THEM

MISNAMING OF 3-D SHAPES

For example: a pyramid as a triangle, a cube as a square, a sphere as a circle.

Encourage the children to name the 2-D shapes of the faces of 3-D shapes. This will help them to see that 3-D shapes are more complex than 2-D ones.

SHAPES IN 'ODD' ORIENTATIONS

Unfortunately, many primary school textbooks only present shapes in obvious orientations. Research shows, for example, that children do not consistently recognize the lower figure as a square:

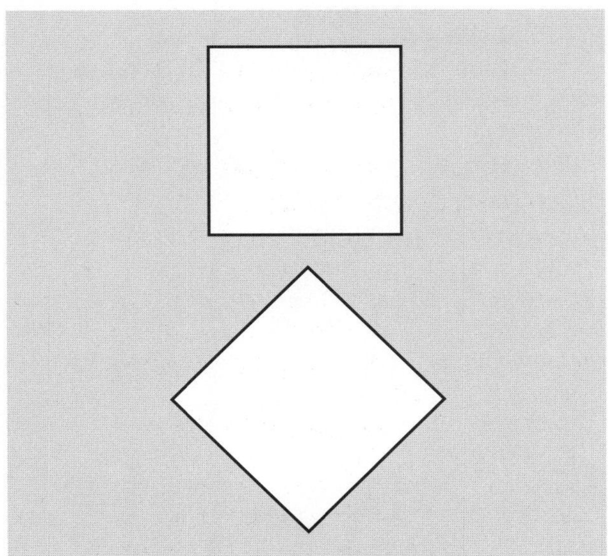

In order to counter this, children need real shapes to manipulate. Use activity sheets to reinforce and consolidate practical activities.

IRREGULAR SHAPES

Similarly, many primary school textbooks only present children with regular shapes. It is important that children know, for example, that all of the shapes below are triangles, not just the one in the top left:

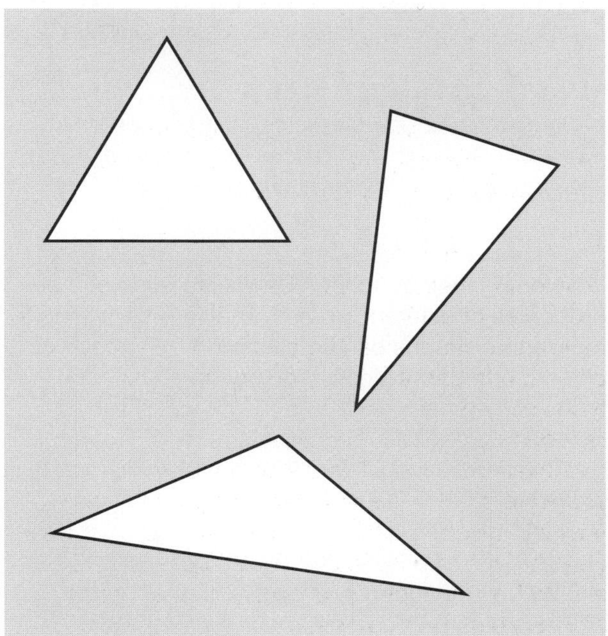

It is important to give children examples of irregular as well as regular shapes.

TESSELLATION

Children often confuse a tessellation with a simple repeating pattern. A tessellation has to cover a surface in a consistent way, in all directions, leaving no gaps. So this is a repeating pattern:

but this is a tessellation:

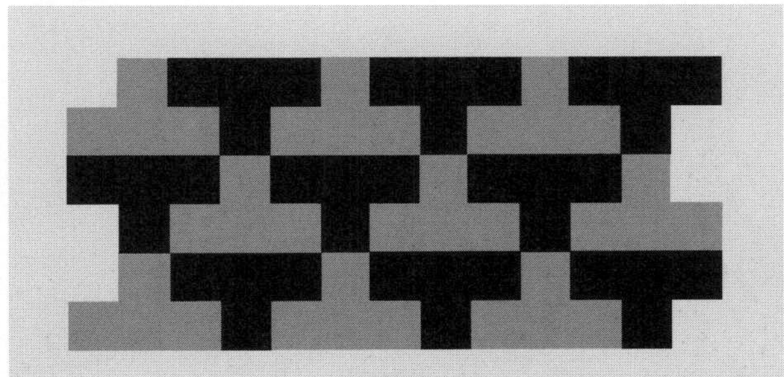

Children should be encouraged to play with real shapes, exploring which ones fit together completely.

SECRET SORT

Whole class
10 minutes (can be repeated frequently)

AIM
To classify shapes according to their properties.

WHAT YOU WILL NEED
Various 2-D and 3-D plastic or card shapes, two large different-coloured pieces of sugar paper. You will need about 12 different shapes for each sort.

WHAT TO DO
This activity can be used repeatedly as a warm-up. Show the children a selection of shapes. Explain that you will be sorting these shapes into two groups; after the first few, the children will have to tell you where each shape should go. Hold up one shape and ask children to describe some of its characteristics. Place it on one of the two pieces of sugar paper. Possible 'secret' criteria include:
- quadrilaterals/triangles
- four or less sides/fewer than four sides
- regular/irregular
- concave/convex
- 2-D/3-D.

Sort three or four shapes to make sure that each group has been clearly represented. Hold up further shapes and ask children to suggest which group they should be placed in. Challenge the children to justify their choices, and ask the rest of the class whether they agree.

The next two **Teacher-directed activities** follow on well from this one.

DISCUSSION QUESTIONS
- *What are the criteria for the two groups?*
- *Is that the only possible answer?*
- *How can you be sure that this shape goes here?*

ASSESSMENT
Are the children able to identify the sorting criteria? Are they able to justify the placement of each shape? If they try the first Extension, are they able to devise and use unambiguous sorting criteria?

EXTENSIONS
- The children can work in groups to decide on sorting criteria, then present the puzzle to the rest of the class.
- Use three groups for sorting (for example: three sides, four sides, more than four sides).

IN THE BAG

Whole class, then groups
50 minutes

AIM
To explore properties of 3-D shapes.

WHAT YOU WILL NEED
Cloth bags, sets of 3-D shapes (such as cubes, cuboids, pyramids, cylinders, cones). You might also want to display a list of the names of these shapes.

WHAT TO DO

Present a bag with some 3-D shapes concealed inside it. Invite a child to put his or her hand in the bag and choose a shape, keeping hold of it inside the bag. The child should then describe what the shape feels like – for example, does it have pointed corners, a curved surface, square or triangular faces? Invite the other children to pose questions to the child holding the shape. After several features of the shape have been established, ask the children to discuss with a partner what the shape could be. When they have all made a prediction, the first child should reveal the shape.

Repeat the activity with the whole class, then split into groups of five or six with a bag of shapes for each group. The children should take it in turn to describe a shape, while the rest of the group try to guess what it is. Finally, bring the class back together and use the discussion questions below to review the activity.

DISCUSSION QUESTIONS

- *What do you know about the shape?*
- *What are good questions to ask?*
- *Which shapes are easy/difficult to work out?*

ASSESSMENT

Do the children use appropriate language to describe the shapes? Do they make sensible deductions from the information they are given?

EXTENSIONS

- Include some 2-D shapes in the bag.
- Include 'real' objects with particular shapes in the bag.
- The children can write descriptions of some of the shapes.

SORT THE SHAPES 1

Whole class or groups
40 minutes

AIM

To classify shapes according to their properties.

WHAT YOU WILL NEED

A large Carroll diagram, either drawn on the board or, ideally, laid out on the carpet using metre sticks (see illustration); sets of shapes relevant to your criteria (at least one for each cell of the diagram); paper, pencils, scissors, rulers; resource page 128. You can include similar shapes of different sizes.

WHAT TO DO

Make sure that the large Carroll diagram is clearly visible to all the children. Choose two pairs of criteria and prepare labels for the cells – for example:

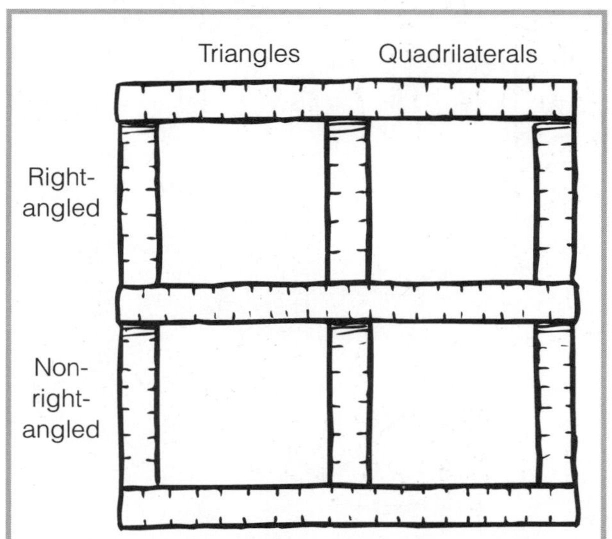

Ask the children to work in pairs. Hold up a shape and ask the children to agree with their partner where in the diagram the shape should be placed. Invite a pair to nominate a place for the shape, then ask the rest of the class whether they agree. When everyone is agreed on the correct answer, put the shape in the cell (use Blu-Tack to fix it if you are using the board) and repeat with a second shape.

After placing nine or ten shapes, ask the children to study the Carroll diagram for a few minutes and then, with their partner, to design one more shape for each cell of the diagram. Their shapes can then be cut out and placed on the main Carroll diagram; alternatively, a group of three pairs can mount their shapes on a new Carroll diagram drawn on sugar paper. The children can use the writing frame on resource page 128 to record the decisions they made when sorting the shapes.

DISCUSSION QUESTIONS

- *How can you be sure that that shape goes there?*
- *What do all these shapes [in any one cell] have in common?*
- *Can anyone think of a shape that we wouldn't be able to place on this diagram?*

ASSESSMENT

Do the children place the shapes correctly on the diagram? Can they design shapes that fit the criteria unambiguously?

EXTENSIONS

- The activity can be repeated using various pairs of criteria, such as: 3 or 4 sides/more than 4 sides, regular/irregular, concave/convex, 2-D/3-D.
- Photocopiable page 25 can be used for individual work to consolidate knowledge of 2-D shapes and angles.

SORT THE SHAPES 2

Whole class or groups
40 minutes

AIM

To classify shapes according to their properties.

WHAT YOU WILL NEED

A large Venn diagram, either drawn on the blackboard or, ideally, laid out on the carpet using PE hoops or similar (see illustration); sets of shapes relevant to your choice of criteria (at least one for each part of the diagram, and some that do not go in either hoop); paper, pencils, scissors, rulers. You can include similar shapes of different sizes.

WHAT TO DO

Make sure that the large Venn diagram is clearly visible to all the children. Choose two pairs of criteria and prepare labels for the hoops – for example:

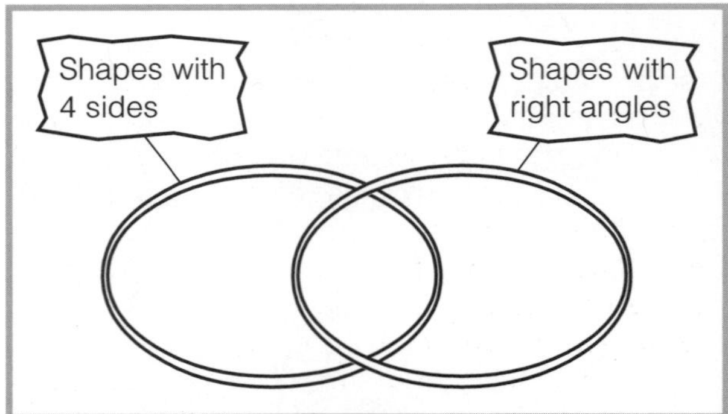

Follow the same procedure as in the previous activity.

DISCUSSION QUESTIONS

- *What can be said about these shapes [in the overlapping section of the diagram]?*
- *What about these [shapes falling outside the two hoops]?*
- *What do all these shapes [in any one hoop] have in common?*
- *How is sorting with the Venn diagram different from sorting with the Carroll diagram? How is it similar?*

ASSESSMENT

Are the children able to place the shapes correctly on the Venn diagram? Are they able to design shapes that fit the different sections of the diagram unambiguously?

EXTENSIONS

- Repeat the activity using a variety of pairs of criteria, such as: shapes with/without symmetry; shapes with sides of equal/not equal length; shapes with at least one right angle/ with no right angles.
- Photocopiable page 26 can be used for individual work to consolidate knowledge of 2-D shapes and angles.

MYSTERY SHAPES

Whole class, then pairs
20 minutes

AIM

To identify shapes, using a range of vocabulary.

WHAT YOU WILL NEED

Resource page 123 – use an enlarged or OHT copy, so the shapes are clearly visible to all. The children need to have a 'maths talk partner'.

WHAT TO DO

This activity is best explained by modelling. Start by giving a description of one of the shapes on page 123 (do not display the sheet yet). Try to use a mixture of formal and informal language – for example: *This shape has five sides; at the top it looks like a rectangle but at the bottom it comes to a point; it's just like an upside-down house.* (Shape G.) After giving the description, ask the children to turn to their partner and see whether they can agree which shape is being described. Note that it is important to establish a 'no calling out' rule for this activity. Ask one pair for their answer, and ask other pairs whether they agree. If there is agreement ask one pair to explain how they decided. If there is disagreement, this should be discussed until all the children are agreed.

Now ask the children to focus on page 123 and think of a description for one shape. After a few minutes, choose someone to describe his or her shape. As before, ask the pairs to agree on which shape is being described. At this stage, both formal statements ('It's got two diagonal lines meeting at a right angle') and informal ones ('It's got two slanty lines'), as well as visual images ('It's like a bow tie') are acceptable. With more practice and experience, children should be encouraged towards formal statements; but informal ones and visual images are important in encouraging them to visualize and internalize the shapes.

DISCUSSION QUESTIONS

- *How can you tell what shape is being described?*
- *Are you sure that is the only shape that fits the description?*

Further discussion can focus on the differences between the 'formal' and 'informal' language that is used to describe the shapes.

ASSESSMENT

Can the children identify the shapes? What kind of language do they use to describe the shapes?

VARIATION

- Create further sheets of shapes to use for this activity; as with page 123, include a mixture of simple and composite or highly irregular shapes.

EXTENSION

- Ask the children to sort the shapes in different ways (see examples in 'Secret sort', page 12).
- Photocopiable page 27 can be used for individual follow-up or assessment work, focusing on written description as well as visualization of shapes.

CUT AND PASTE

Whole class
50 minutes

AIM

To investigate how shapes can be combined to make new shapes.

WHAT YOU WILL NEED

For each child: a paper or thin card oblong (A4 or A5), a ruler, scissors.

WHAT TO DO

Ask the children to fold their paper diagonally (or draw a line across it) and then cut it from corner to corner. Now ask them join the triangles back together to recreate the rectangle. Check that everyone can do this. Now ask the children to flip one of the triangles over and join the two sides that were the long sides of the rectangle. What shapes have been made?

Ask the children to find out what shapes can be made by joining the two triangles along any two matching sides. After they have investigated for a while, ask them to show you the shapes (you could draw them on the board). There are six possible solutions (see illustration). This activity also illustrates an important principle about the conservation of area (see the 'Length and area' section); but here, the emphasis is on creative rearrangement of shapes.

Now remove the 'matching sides' restriction and ask the children to create other shapes – for example, with points joined or with overlaps. This opens up a new range of creative possibilities, and sets up the class well for the 'Take this tangram' activity (page 22).

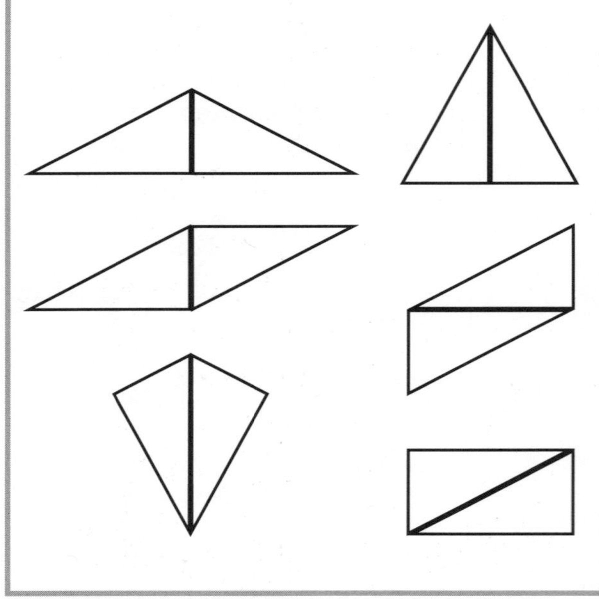

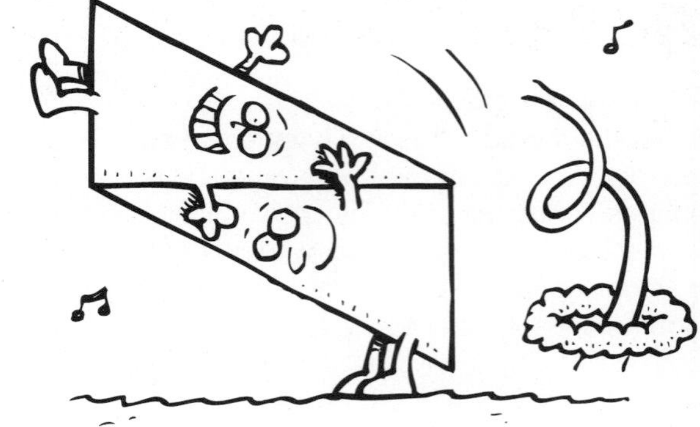

DISCUSSION QUESTIONS

- *What is similar/different about these shapes?*
- *Can you name the shapes you've made?*

ASSESSMENT

Can the children find all the different composite shapes? Can they name the shapes (triangle, parallelogram, oblong or rectangle, kite)?

VARIATION

- Use a square rather than oblong piece of paper.
- Cut the paper along both diagonals.
- Ask groups of children to mount their created shapes on sugar paper. This will make an excellent display, illustrating the conservation of area.

EXTENSION

The children can use the writing frame (resource page 128) to give an account of the ways in which they used the triangles to make new shapes. Their writing could be displayed alongside the mounted shapes.

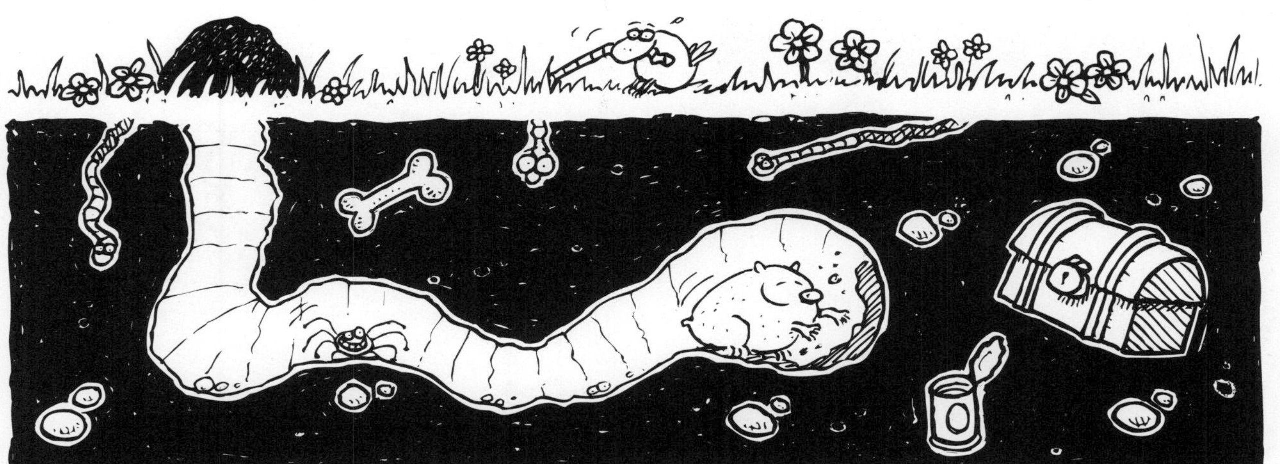

CROSS-SECTIONS

Whole class or groups
30 minutes

AIM

To visualize 2-D cross-sections of 3-D shapes.

WHAT YOU WILL NEED

A selection of 3-D shapes (cube, sphere, pyramid, cylinder, cone), Plasticine or play dough, modelling knives.

WHAT TO DO

Hold up the 3-D shapes in turn and check that the children know the name of each one. Now hold up a sphere and ask the children to imagine making a straight-edged cut through the middle, from top to bottom. *What shape will be created on the surface (where you make the cut)?* Ask children for their predictions. *What if you cut from left to right through the middle? What about left to right near the top?*

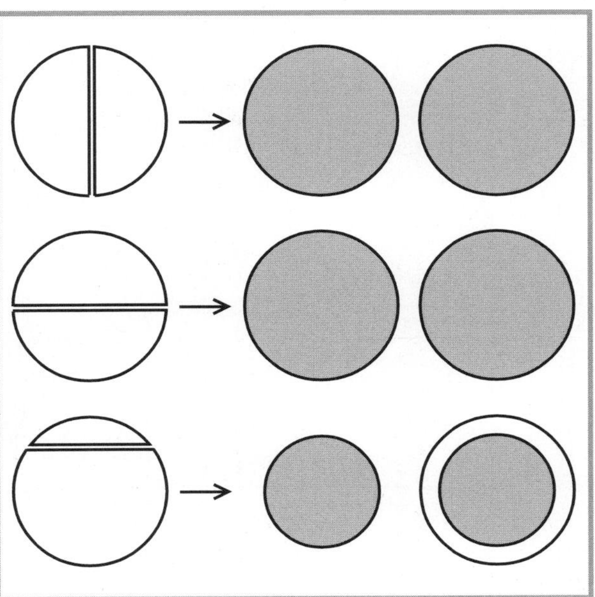

Ask the children to make a variety of Plasticine shapes and predict the effect of cutting them in various ways, then try it with a knife. Examples could include: a sphere (see below); a cube (slice corners); a pyramid (slice off the tip, slice down from the tip); a cylinder (cut from top to bottom); a cone (cut across at different points). It is important that the children make predictions (visualize the likely result of the cut) before actually doing it. Asking them to write down or sketch the expected result is a good strategy here.

DISCUSSION QUESTIONS

- *What will happen when I make this cut?*
- *Can you explain why you will see a circle/square/ triangle when you make that cut?*

ASSESSMENT

Are the children able to name the 3-D shapes? Can they predict the 2-D shape made by each cut?

EXTENSIONS

- The children can experiment with making slices at different angles. For example, when a sphere is cut at an angle, does a circle always result?
- The children can make a selection of Plasticine 3-D shapes, then find out which ones can be cut to make specific 2-D shapes such as squares, rectangles, circles and ellipses.

SHAPE DETECTIVES

Whole class, then groups
30 minutes, then repeated 10-minute game

AIMS

To visualize 2-D shapes. To identify their key properties.

WHAT YOU WILL NEED

A selection of large card 2-D shapes (see list on page 8), a large screen (such as a board), smaller screens (such as large books).

WHAT TO DO

Stand behind a screen and wave a 2-D shape back and forth in an arc while lifting it slowly, so that it gradually emerges into view (see illustration). As the shape first begins to emerge, ask the children what shape it might be. Reveal more of the shape and ask again. It is also useful to ask them what shape it is definitely **not**. Gradually reveal more and more of the shape until the children seem certain; then display the shape fully. Repeat several times with different shapes, or with the same shape (such as an oblong) in a different orientation. Before repeating, encourage reflection (see 'Discussion questions').

Later, the children can play the game in pairs with sets of smaller plastic shapes and a smaller screen between them.

DISCUSSION QUESTIONS

- *What could the shape be?*
- *What shape is it definitely not?*
- *When were you sure what shape it was?*
- *When did you change your mind? Why?*

ASSESSMENT

Can the children make sensible predictions? Can they identify the key characteristics (such as number of sides, regularity) of 2-D shapes?

EXTENSION

Play the game again, asking the children to sketch what they think the whole shape will be after part of it has been revealed.

CIRCLES

Whole class
50 minutes

AIMS
To draw circles using compasses. To introduce the vocabulary 'centre', 'radius' and 'diameter'.

WHAT YOU WILL NEED
Compasses, sharp pencils, paper.

WHAT TO DO
Show the children a circle and ask them what would be difficult about drawing a circle (compared to a square or triangle). *Why wouldn't a ruler be helpful?*

Now show the children a pair of compasses and ask if anyone has seen one before. Demonstrate to the class how it can be used, emphasizing the need to:
- mark the centre of the circle before starting
- make sure that the compasses point and pencil tip are aligned
- hold the paper carefully to stop it moving while you turn the compass around.

Explain that the distance (called the **radius**) between the compass point and the pencil tip shouldn't be changed while you are drawing the circle. After reminders about safety (compass tips are very sharp!), let the children practise using the compasses. When they have got the knack of drawing circles, set them specific tasks – for example, drawing circles of specific radii or creating patterns (the illustration shows a few examples).

In the plenary session, ask the children how they could find the distance across a whole circle – that is, from the edge and through the centre to the edge on the opposite side. Explain that this is called the **diameter** of a circle; can children see how it relates to the radius? (If the children are familiar with the word **perimeter**, you can use that word for the edge of the circle and explain that the perimeter of a circle has a special name: the **circumference**.)

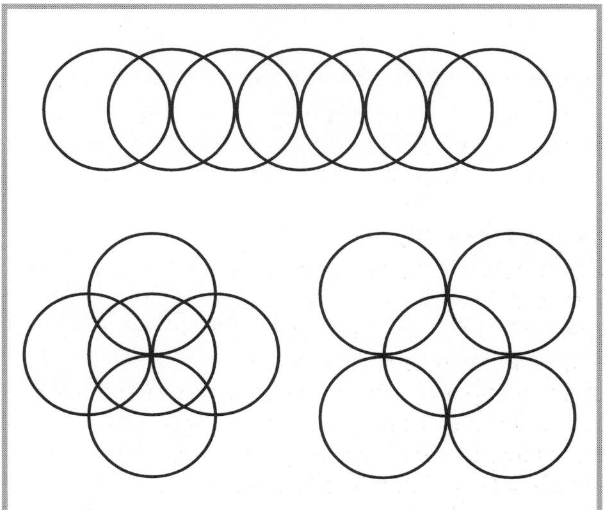

DISCUSSION QUESTIONS
- *Why is it difficult to draw a circle with a ruler?*
- *What do you need to do to draw a good circle with compasses?*
- *What is the relationship between the diameter and the radius of a circle?*

ASSESSMENT POINTER
Can the children use compasses to draw a circle, appreciating the potential difficulties? Can they name features of a circle (centre, radius, diameter), and understand why the diameter of any circle is always twice its radius?

EXTENSIONS
- The children can use an ICT drawing package to create circle patterns (the patterns shown above were all created using such a program).
- They can try measuring the circumference of their circles (see 'All the way round' in the 'Length and area' section, page 88). At this stage it is not necessary to make a formal connection between circumference and radius; however, able children may notice that the circumference is always just over 3 times the diameter.
- Photocopiable page 31 provides further individual practice in drawing circles and measuring the radius and diameter.
- The children can use the radius/diameter relationship as a context for practising doubling and halving during a mental maths session.

QUADRILATERALS

Whole class, working in pairs
50 minutes

AIM

To identify and compare various types of quadrilateral.

WHAT YOU WILL NEED

Geoboards (ideally 3 × 3, or section off areas of larger geoboards), record sheets (resource page 124, or use cm squared dotty paper), pencils, a sheet of sugar paper (or OHT of the record sheet).

WHAT TO DO

Give the children appropriate guidance regarding the safe use of elastic bands. Ask them to work in pairs, making different quadrilaterals (that is, any shape with four sides) on the geoboards, and then to compare their quadrilaterals with another pair's. What is the same about the quadrilaterals? What is different about them?

Ask each pair to make a further different quadrilateral and compare it with another pair's.

By this time, the children should appreciate that many different quadrilaterals can be made. Ask them how many unique quadrilaterals they think could be made, not including rotations and reflections. Now ask each pair to find and record four or five different quadrilaterals. There are in fact 16 possible different quadrilaterals (see illustration below), but it is not necessary for any one pair to find them all.

After each pair has recorded several examples, call the class together and ask each pair in turn to draw one of their quadrilaterals on the prepared class recording sheet. The non-uniqueness of rotations and reflections may need to be reinforced at this point. When about 12 different quadrilaterals have been recorded, use some of the questions below to focus the children's attention on the properties of different quadrilaterals.

DISCUSSION QUESTIONS

- *What is different about those two quadrilaterals?*
- *Which quadrilaterals have... a right angle? ...more than one right angle? ...parallel sides?*
- *Which are concave?*
- *Which have special names? [square, oblong, kite, parallelogram, trapezium]*

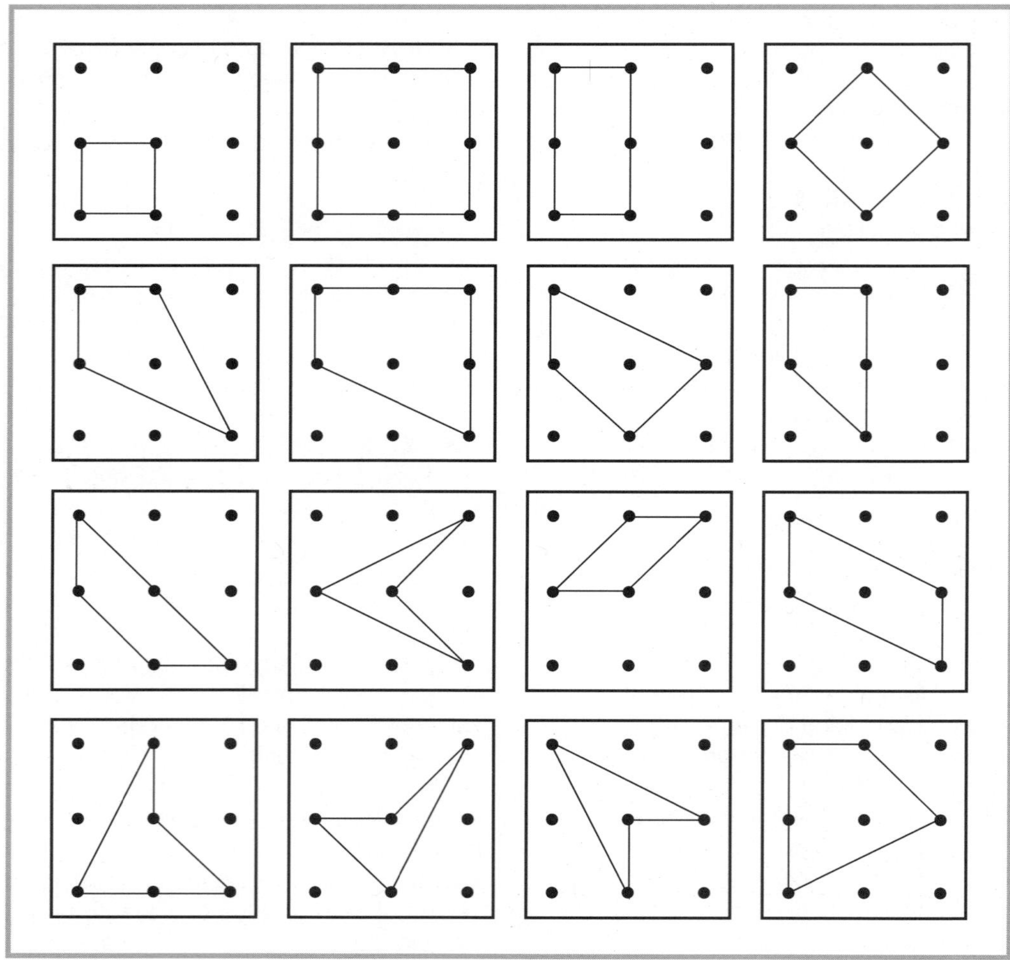

ASSESSMENT
Are the children able to find a selection of different quadrilaterals? Are they able to describe and discuss the properties of the quadrilaterals?

VARIATION
- The children can find different triangles on a 3 × 3 pinboard.

EXTENSIONS
- The children can find quadrilaterals on a 4 × 4 pinboard.
- They can use photocopiable page 30 for follow-up work on shape properties.

MY BOX

Groups, then pairs
50 minutes

AIMS
To look at the relationship between 2-D and 3-D shapes. To visualize nets.

WHAT YOU WILL NEED
A selection of cardboard boxes such as cereal boxes (have the children collect these for a couple of weeks beforehand), scissors, glue, paper, pencils. Take two identical cardboard boxes and carefully unfold one to show its net.

WHAT TO DO
Explain that this lesson is about investigating the way boxes are made. Give each group two or three boxes, and ask them to make a sketch of one box. Ask them to consider why this is more difficult than sketching a simple 2-D shape. You could discuss techniques for perspective drawing, but the main point is to make them focus on the 3-D box shape.

Now show the children the box and box net that you have prepared. Discuss the characteristics of the net: the constituent 2-D shapes, the folds and the overlaps. Now ask the children to focus on the box they have sketched and to imagine what its net will look like. They should talk to their neighbour about what the net will look like, then make a drawing of the net. The important thing to emphasize is the relationship between the sides, not the scale of the drawing.

Next, ask the children in pairs to open up their boxes, pulling the sides apart carefully and using scissors if necessary. They can then compare the net with their sketch. Finally, they should fold the net back up and glue the box back together. The boxes can then be swapped around for a repeat of the activity at another time.

DISCUSSION QUESTIONS
- *What is a good way to draw that shape?*
- *What 2-D shapes will you see in the net?*
- *How do the nets compare with your predictions?*

ASSESSMENT POINTER
Are the children able to make reasonably accurate sketches? Can they identify the 2-D shapes that form the faces of the box?

EXTENSIONS
- After sketching the net, the children can use card to make a similar box.
- More confident children can use less regular boxes, such as certain types of chocolate box.
- Photocopiable page 28 can be used to consolidate, extend or assess the children's awareness of shape nets.
- The children can use the writing frame on resource page 128 to give an account of their work.

3-D CONSTRUCTION

Whole class or groups, working in pairs
50 minutes

AIM
To develop familiarity with 3-D objects.

WHAT YOU WILL NEED
Commercial resources for modelling 3-D shapes, such as Polydron, Clixi or Connect-o-Straws (alternatively, use straws and plasticine); some 3-D solid shapes such as cubes, cuboids, pyramids and tetrahedrons, enough for at least one between two. The cardboard boxes from 'My box' (see above) could also be used.

WHAT TO DO

Distribute the 3-D shapes and ask the children to discuss their features – for example, the number and type of faces, edges and vertices. Encourage pairs to compare different 3-D shapes: what is similar and different about them?

Make available a selection of modelling materials; ask the children to use these to recreate one of the 3-D shapes. Different groups can use different materials in order to focus on different aspects: with Polydron or Clixi, the 2-D shapes of the faces is most important; with Connect-o-Straws, the edges and vertices become the focus.

DISCUSSION QUESTIONS

- *What 2-D shapes can you see on the surface of your 3-D shape?*
- *How is this shape like/unlike that one?*
- *Which 3-D shape has the most vertices/the most edges?*

ASSESSMENT

Do the children distinguish clearly between the names of 2-D and of 3-D shapes? Can they make models of the 3-D shapes?

EXTENSIONS

- The children can use nets to create 3-D shapes.
- More formally, they can tabulate the numbers of faces, edges and vertices for a range of 3-D shapes. This might lead the most able children to discover that faces + vertices = edges + 2.

TAKE THIS TANGRAM

Whole class or group, working in pairs
50 minutes

AIM

To see how shapes can be combined to make new shapes.

WHAT YOU WILL NEED

A set of tangram pieces (resource page 125) for each child, ideally photocopied onto card and labelled with the child's initials; a set of tangram pictures (enlarge the bottom strip of page 125). More tangram pictures can be found in books of mathematical puzzles.

WHAT TO DO

Tell the children that the **tangram** is an ancient Chinese puzzle: a square cut into seven shapes. Let them spend some time becoming familiar with the tangram pieces. They could cut out their own sets from copies of page 125. (Alternatively, they could start with the pieces.) They should compare and name the seven pieces. Now ask them to work in pairs to recreate the original square. (There are several different ways of doing this.)

Show the children some examples of pictures made with the tangram pieces. Working in pairs, they should try to recreate these pictures or use them as a basis for their own designs.

DISCUSSION QUESTIONS

- *How do the shapes relate to each other?*
- *What is a good way to solve the puzzle?*

ASSESSMENT POINTER

Can the children name the individual shapes? Can they recreate the tangram pictures?

VARIATION

- Less able children can use a selection of the seven pieces to make pictures.

EXTENSIONS

- The children can make their own tangram sets by dividing a square into pieces in different ways.
- For further tangram activities, see the 'Position and direction' section (page 53) and the 'Length and area' section (page 83).

MAKE IT FIT

Groups of 6–8, working in pairs
50 minutes

AIM
To explore shapes that tessellate.

WHAT YOU WILL NEED
Sets of plastic shapes, A3 paper, pencils, examples of tessellating patterns. If your supply of a particular shape is limited, draw around one fair-sized example several times on a sheet of paper and photocopy onto card; the children can then cut out their own set of shapes.

WHAT TO DO
Provide several sets of identical 2-D shapes for each group to choose from (triangles, quadrilaterals or any polyominoes – those shown in the 'Transformation and symmetry' section, page 40 are good ones to start with). Ask the children, working in pairs, to create patterns by fitting several of the same shape together. Explain that **tessellating patterns** are when the same pattern is repeated over and over in every direction, with no gaps, as in a tiling design (see note on page 11).

After some time, stop the class and ask them to describe their patterns. Now ask the children to create a second pattern (they might like to recreate one that another pair have described) and record it on a sheet of A3 paper. They should do this by taking one shape and using it as a template to draw around, continuing the pattern until the paper is filled up. (They might prefer to do this individually.) More able children could try making patterns from combinations of two shapes.

Ask the children to colour their completed pattern, and to describe in words how they created it. Encourage them to take great care with their final designs, as you will use these for a class display of tessellating patterns.

DISCUSSION QUESTIONS
- *Can you describe this pattern?*
- *Which shapes can fit together in different ways?*
- *What makes an interesting tessellation pattern?*

ASSESSMENT
Can the children create tessellating patterns and distinguish them from non-tessellating patterns? Can they use appropriate language to describe how the shapes fit together?

EXTENSIONS
- The children can use two different shapes to make a tessellating pattern.
- Include some shapes which won't tessellate in the starting collection. Can the children find out which shapes will tessellate and which won't?
- Photocopiable page 29 provides work on tile patterns, consolidating the idea of tessellation.
- The children can use appropriate computer software to create tessellating patterns – for example, *VersaTile* or *Tesselmania*.

GEOSTRIP SHAPES

Whole class or group, working in pairs
30 minutes

AIM
To explore different triangles and quadrilaterals.

WHAT YOU WILL NEED
Geostrips (commercially available, or made from resource page 127 copied onto card and covered with sticky-backed plastic), split-pin paper fasteners, pencils, rulers, paper. Each child will need several geostrips of each size.

WHAT TO DO
Show the children how the geostrips can be joined together to make a triangle, then a quadrilateral. Demonstrate how you can use different-sized geostrips to create different triangles and quadrilaterals, as well as shapes with more sides.

Now let the children work in pairs to explore different shapes with the geostrips. They should be set a target number of different shapes to create, depending on their ability. Each new shape should be sketched and labelled with its name.

Call the class together to review the work done, using the 'Discussion questions' below. The discussion should review the names of the different shapes, and confirm that shapes such as pentagons and hexagons do not have to be regular. For triangles, the terms **equilateral** (three sides the same) and **isosceles** (two sides the same) can be introduced. For quadrilaterals, use the names **parallelogram**, **rhombus** and **kite** as well as the more familiar **square** and **oblong** (which are both types of **rectangle**).

DISCUSSION QUESTIONS
- *What are your shapes called? How do you know?*
- *Which triangles have the same length/different-length strips?*
- *Which quadrilaterals have the same length strips? Which have two different-length strips?*
- *Which shapes are the most rigid? Why?*

ASSESSMENT
Can the children create a range of different triangles and quadrilaterals using the strips? Can they name the different shapes and describe the properties of each?

EXTENSIONS
- The children can use geostrips to explore triangles, quadrilaterals or shapes with more than four sides.
- They can use photocopiable page 30 to consolidate their knowledge of the properties of shapes.

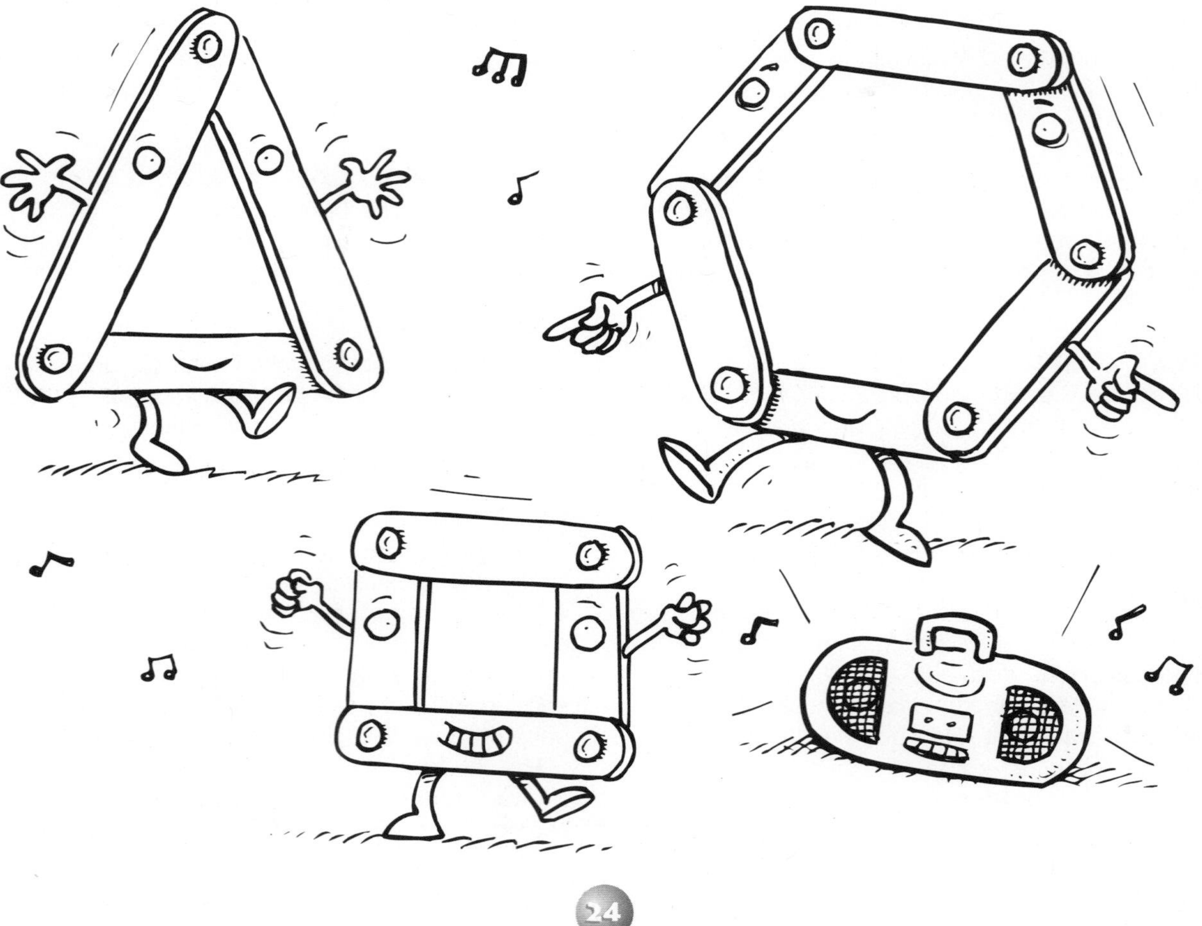

NAME DATE

PLACE THE SHAPES 1

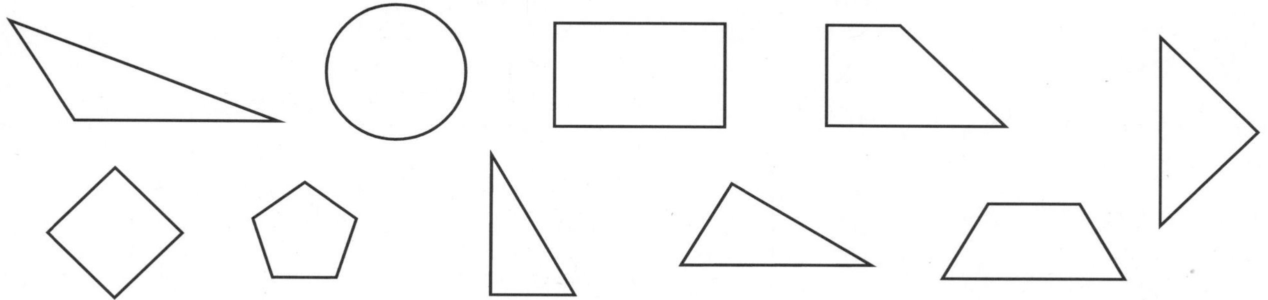

■ Draw each of these shapes in the correct cell of the Carroll diagram.

	Triangles	Quadrilaterals
Right-angled		
Non-right-angled		

Use the back of the sheet to answer these questions:

1. Which two shapes do not fit onto the diagram? Can you explain why?

2. Which shapes were easy to place? Which ones were trickier?

SEE 'SORT THE SHAPES 1', PAGE 13.

NAME DATE

PLACE THE SHAPES 2

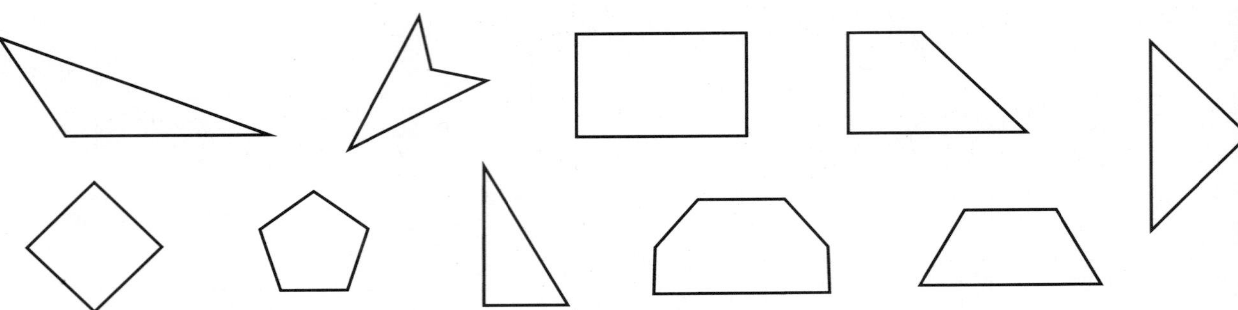

■ Draw each of these shapes in the correct section of the Venn diagram.

SHAPES WITH 4 SIDES SHAPES WITH RIGHT ANGLES

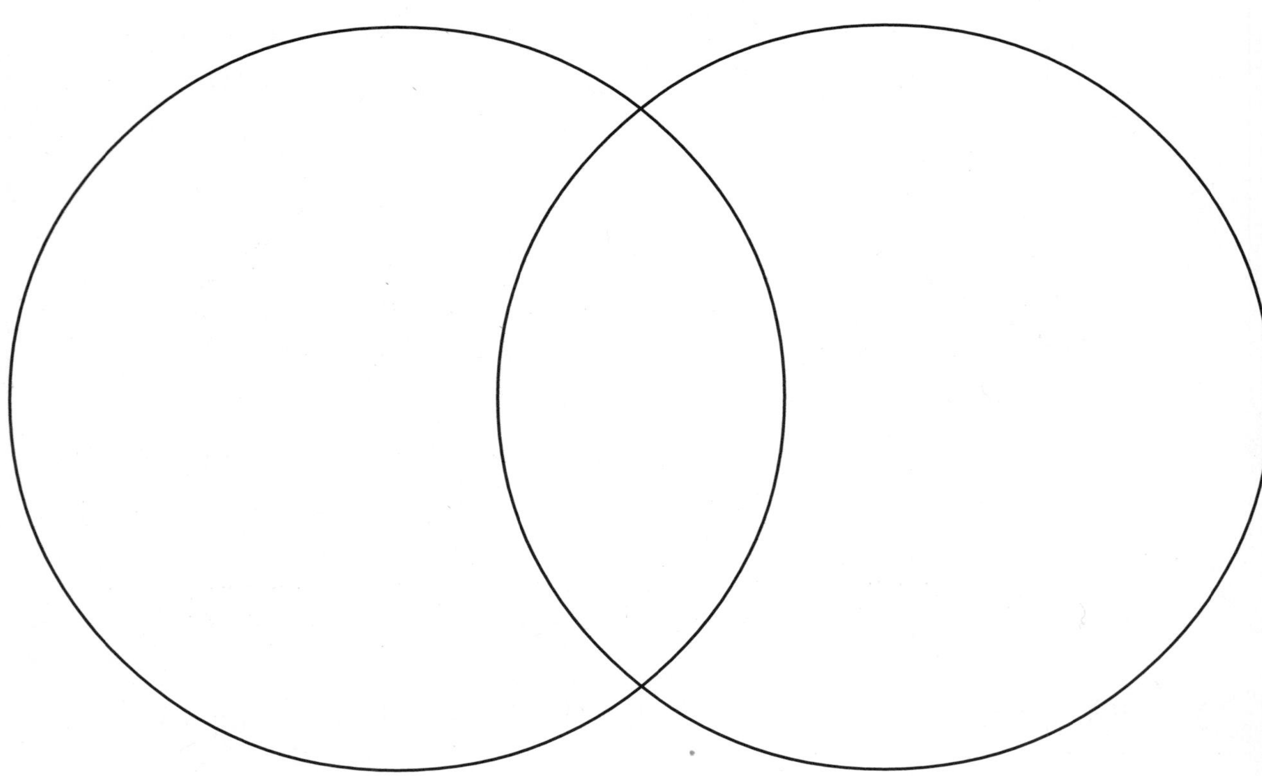

Choose one shape from each section of the Venn diagram. On the back of this sheet, copy the shape and write down what you know about it.

SEE 'SORT THE SHAPES 2', PAGE 14.

NAME DATE

DESCRIBE ME!

■ Write a description of each of these shapes.

■ Read your descriptions (in any order) to a friend. Can your friend guess which shape you are describing each time?

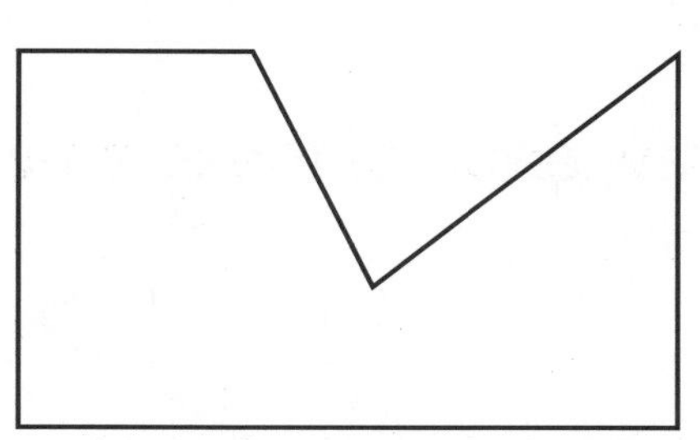
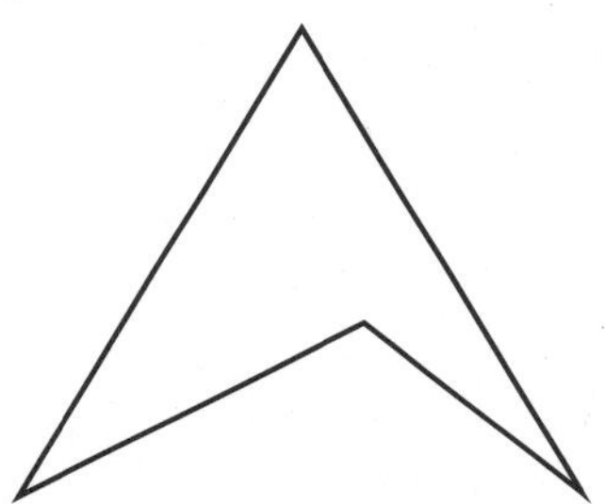
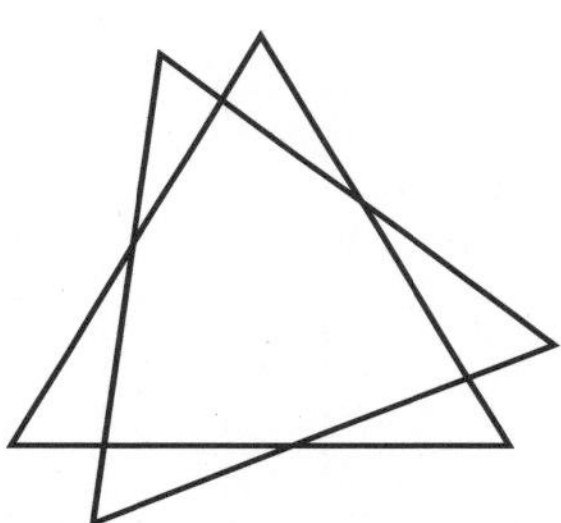
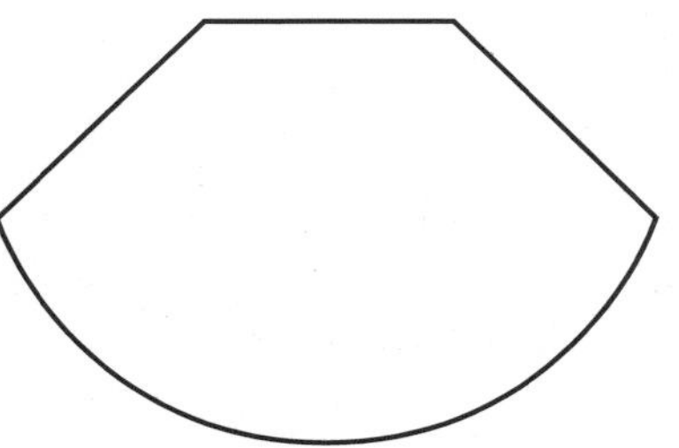
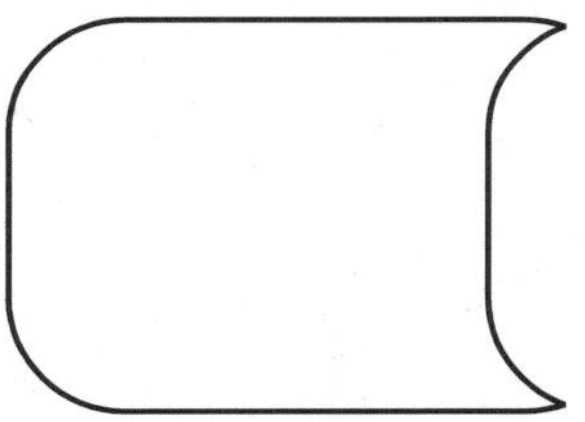

 Which shapes are easy to describe? Why? Tell your friend.

SEE 'MYSTERY SHAPES', PAGE 15.

NAME DATE

SHAPE NETS

■ Draw pictures on the back of this sheet to show what 3-D shapes these nets would make if they were cut out and folded.

■ Write down what each 3-D shape is called.

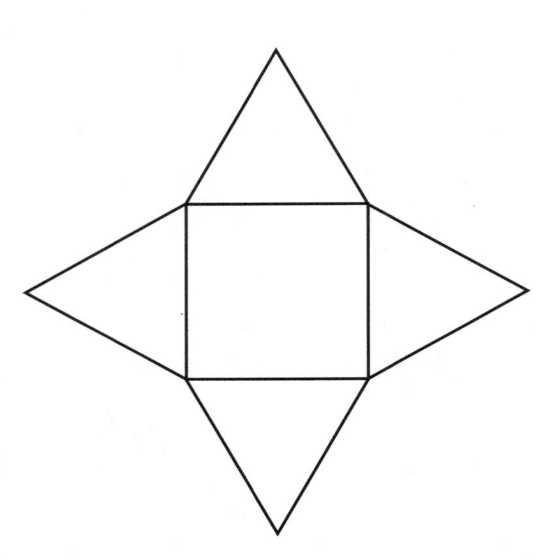

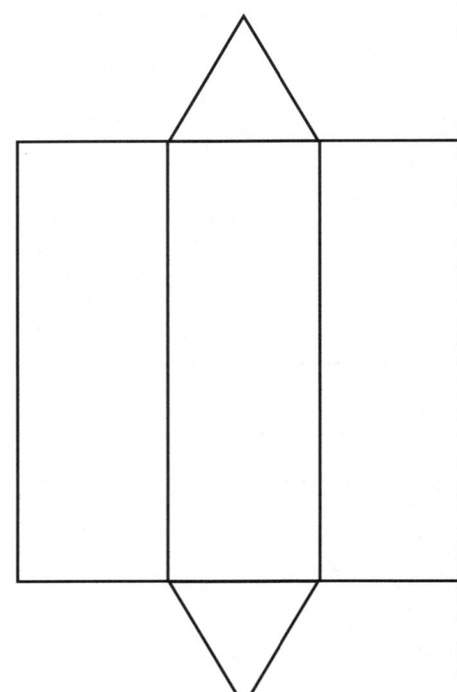

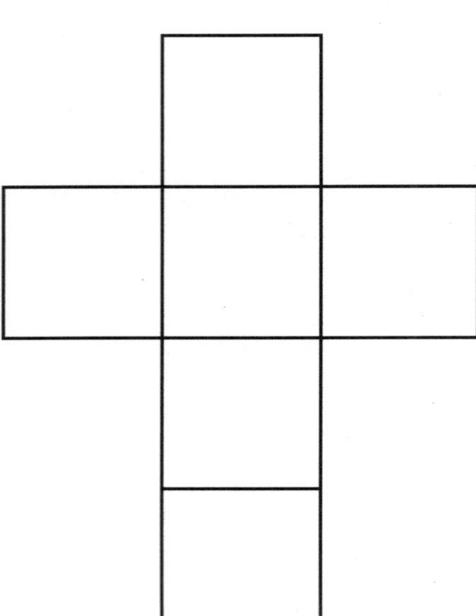

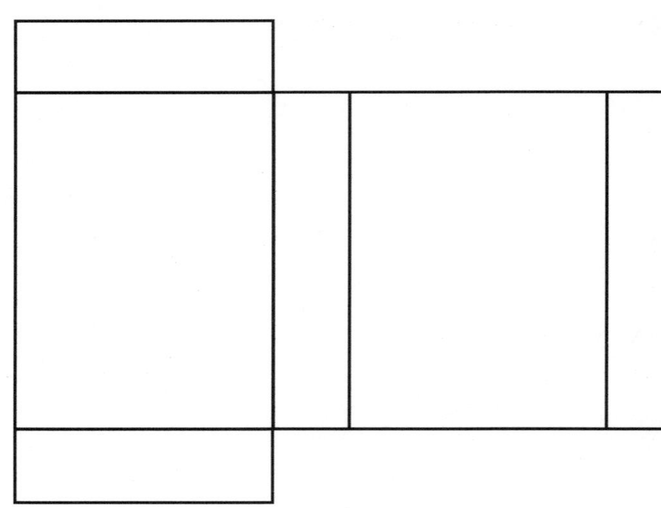

Which shape did you find the most difficult to draw? Why? Does your friend agree?

SEE 'MY BOX', PAGE 21.

NAME DATE

FOLLOW THE PATTERN

■ Carefully continue each of these patterns:

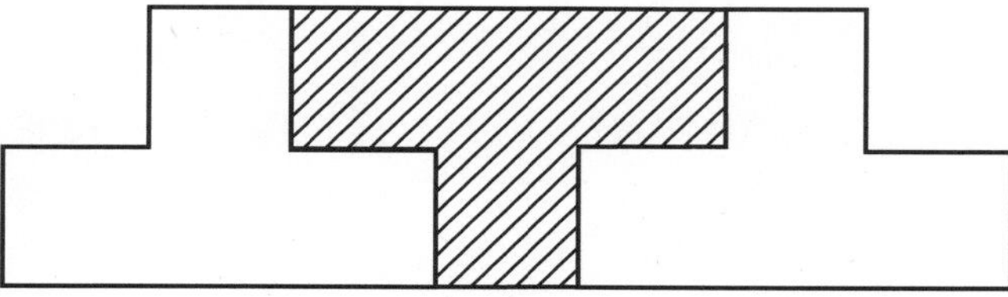

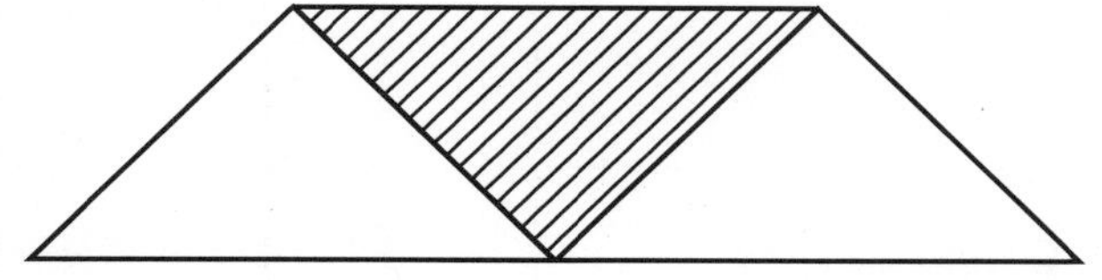

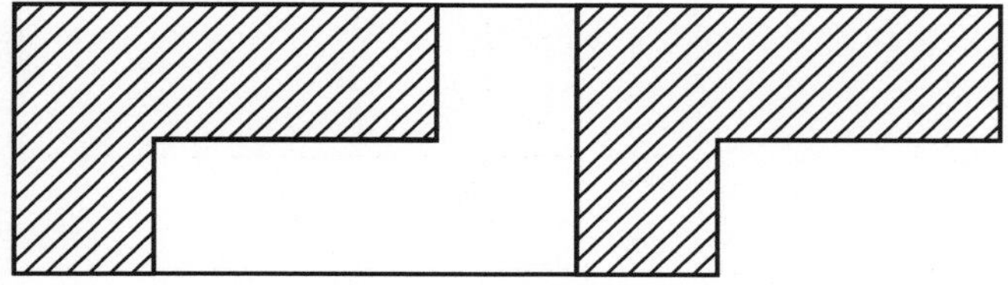

Now make up another pattern of your own:

Which is your favourite shape? Why?

SEE 'MAKE IT FIT', PAGE 23.

NAME DATE

TRUE OR FALSE?

■ Which of these statements are true, and which are false? Give reasons for your answers, using words or pictures.

1. All shapes with four sides are called squares. **True / False**

2. All rectangles have four right angles. **True / False**

3. Triangles are three-dimensional. **True / False**

4. Hexagons have more sides than pentagons. **True / False**

Make up some more questions like these for your friends. Write them on the back of this sheet.

SEE 'GEOSTRIP SHAPES', PAGE 24

NAME DATE

MORE CIRCLES

■ Measure the radius and diameter of these circles:

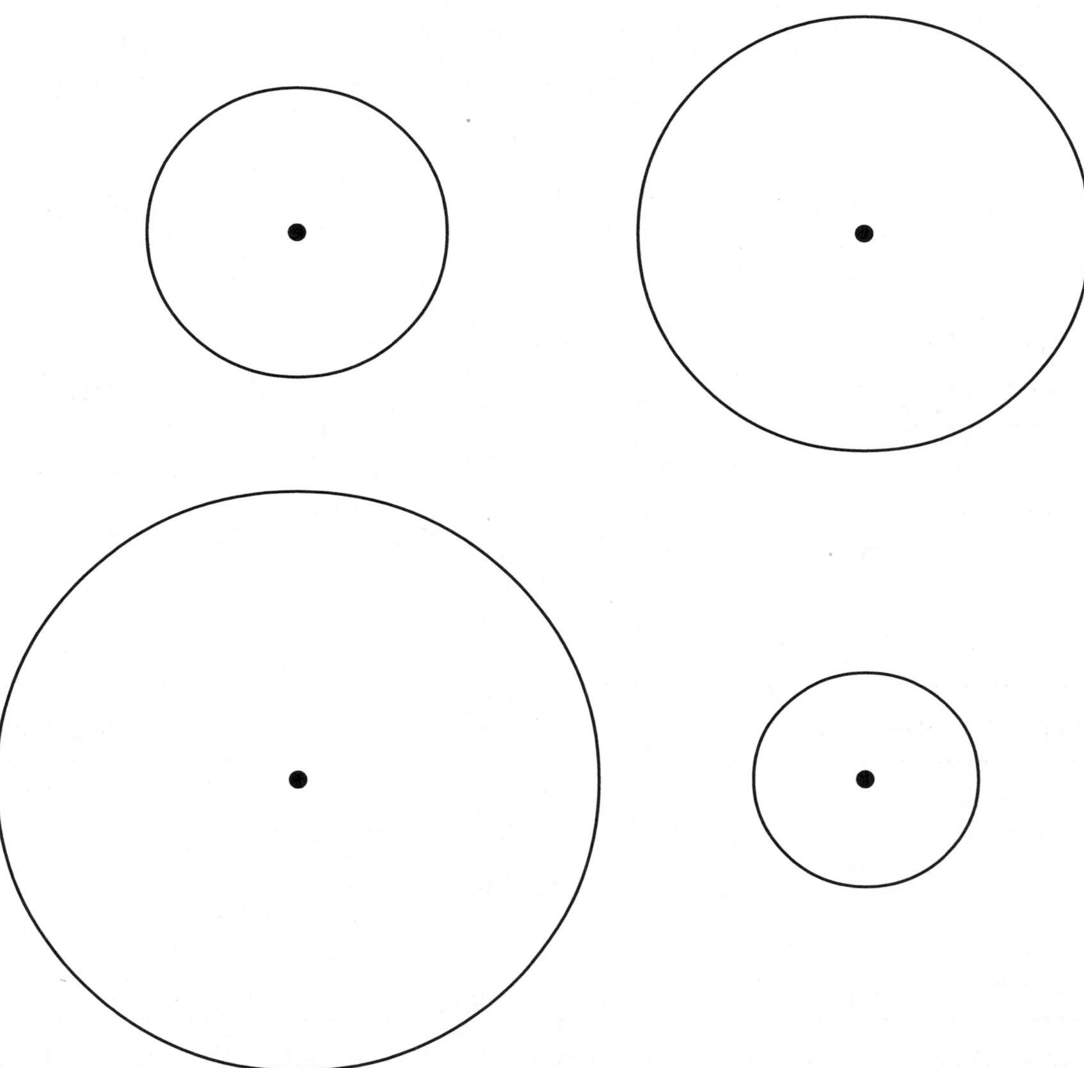

■ Explain in your own words how to find the radius and diameter of a circle.

Choose one of the circles. On the back of this sheet, draw two more circles: one with twice and one with half the radius of your chosen circle.

SEE 'CIRCLES', PAGE 19.

KEY IDEAS

- Understanding that shapes can be transformed in a variety of ways.
- Knowing that rotating and reflecting shapes creates different effects with different shapes.
- Knowing that a line of symmetry in a shape can be horizontal or vertical.
- Using ICT to develop understanding of this theme.

The following are all types of transformation. It is important that children in this age group experience each type, and that they learn to distinguish rotations from reflections.

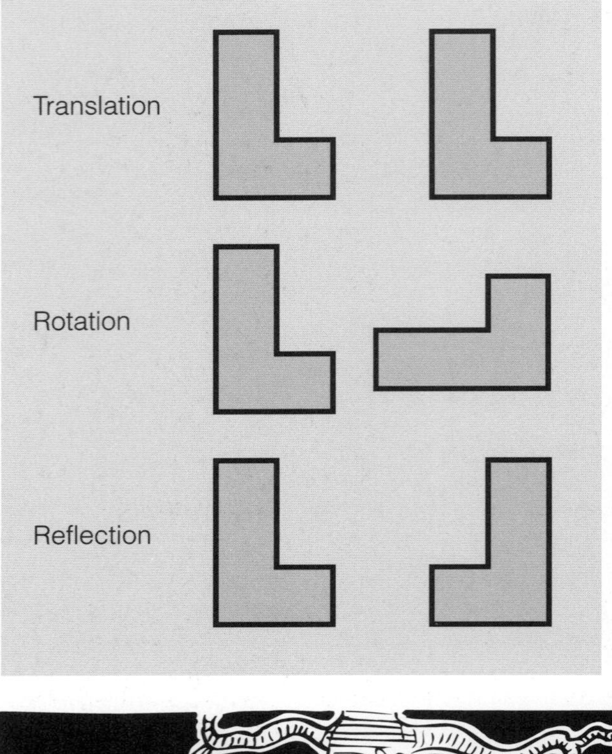

Reflections are best investigated using mirrors. A plane mirror image shows children that a whole shape or picture is reversed by reflection. The mirror also provides a **line of symmetry**. At this stage, concentrate on horizontal and vertical lines of symmetry. Children should be exploring symmetry as an attribute of various 2-D shapes; this is a natural progression from earlier work on pictures of symmetrical objects such as butterflies and fir trees.

Rotations are linked to children's developing understanding of **angle** as a measure of turn. Turning shapes by one, two or three right angles produces a range of different effects. **Rotational symmetry** refers specifically to a shape having an identical appearance after being turned. Thus an equilateral triangle, a square and a regular pentagon have a rotational symmetry of 3, 4 and 5 respectively. At this stage, it is useful to work with tracing paper: a shape can be traced and the paper turned to observe the effects.

Translation refers to a straight-line move in any direction. At this stage, vertical and horizontal translations are sufficient. The word 'slide' can be used.

SOME COMMON MISCONCEPTIONS AND STRATEGIES FOR CORRECTING THEM

PLACING REFLECTIONS

Research has shown that children find reflecting a shape in a mirror line difficult without any additional points of reference:

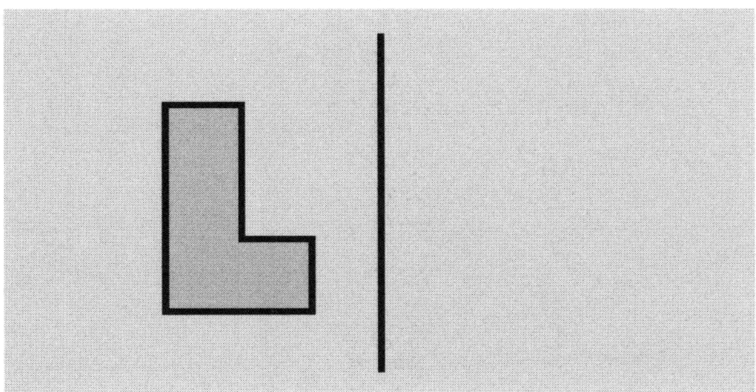

Using a squared grid for work on transformations can have a positive effect:

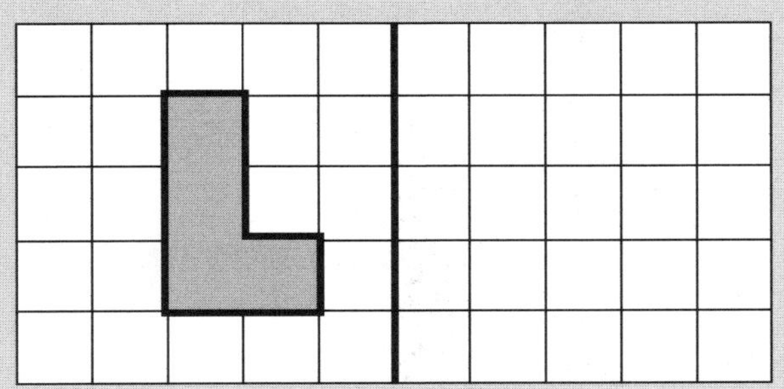

Children could try reflecting a shape first on a squared grid and then on plain paper.

TRANSLATION OR REFLECTION?

Children often confuse translation (see figure) with reflection.

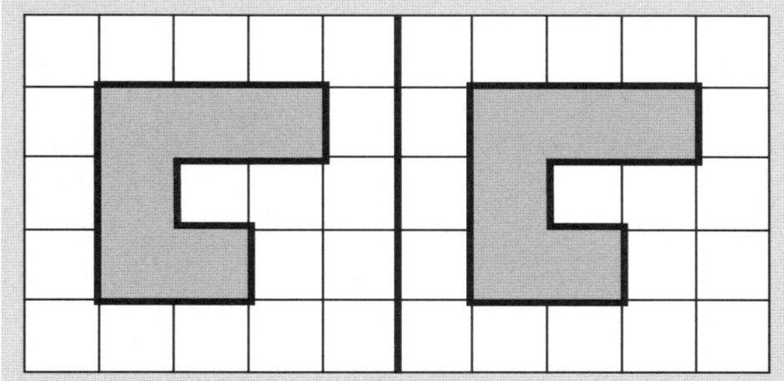

Children need to experience both processes in a practical context (for example, by working with mirrors).

ROTATION OR REFLECTION?

Children often confuse rotation with reflection, particularly in cases where the result is the same. Compare rotating the shape below by 90° to reflecting it vertically:

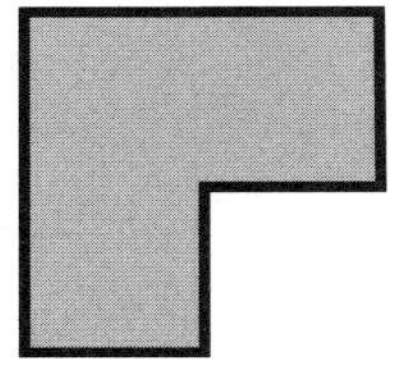

Tackle each concept separately, talking all the time about **turning** (rotation) and **mirror images** (reflection).

BY THE END OF Y3/P4, MOST CHILDREN SHOULD BE ABLE TO:

- identify and sketch lines of symmetry in simple shapes, and recognize shapes with no lines of symmetry
- sketch the reflection of a simple shape in a mirror line
- make and describe right-angled turns
- investigate a statement made about a shape by finding examples that satisfy it (for example, regarding the symmetry of a particular kind of shape).

BY THE END OF Y4/P5, MOST CHILDREN SHOULD BE ABLE TO:

- sketch the reflection of a simple shape in a mirror line parallel to one side of the shape
- recognize and draw examples of horizontal and vertical lines of symmetry
- make and investigate a general statement about familiar shapes (see above).

CUT AND SEE

Whole class, then individual work.
50 minutes

AIM

To explore the use of a line of symmetry to generate a pattern.

WHAT YOU WILL NEED

Plain A4 paper, scissors, rulers, pencils, resource page 128.

WHAT TO DO

This activity is best explained by demonstration. Fold a piece of A4 paper in half, lengthways. Using the fold in the paper as the base, draw a pattern from the base: several short connected lines, finally returning to the base.

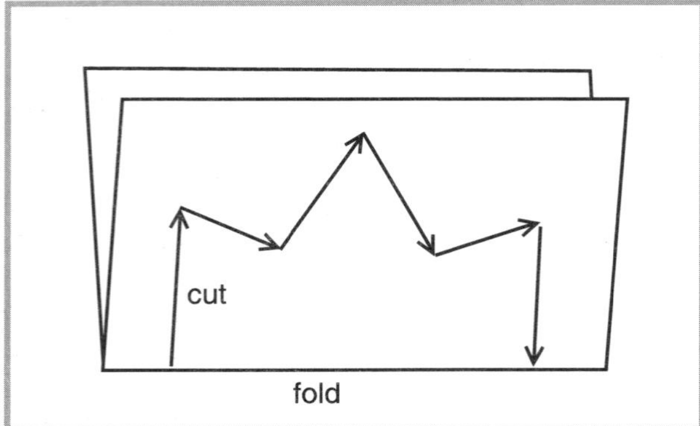

Tell the children that you are going to cut along these lines. Ask them to predict what the cut-out shape will look like. Now cut along the lines, carefully and slowly (remember that you are modelling the activity), starting and ending at the base. Ask the children to predict what will happen when you unfold the paper. Most should realise that you will have a 'mirror pattern' of your cut-out shape; encourage them to describe what the whole cut-out will look like. Try again with different cuts, again giving the children time to visualize the resultant pattern.

Now distribute paper, pencils and scissors; if you would like the children to use straight lines, they will need rulers. Ask them to create a symmetrical pattern as you did. They should work in groups, asking their peers to predict what the pattern will look like. When they have finished, gather the class together and ask some to show their designs.

Repeat the exercise, but with a particular theme (or set groups different tasks) – for example:

- Creating a specific object, identifiable by its symmetry – a rocket, fir tree, house, person and so on.
- Creating an artistic design made up only of curved lines.
- Focusing on shapes – can the children create shapes (with 3–8 sides) that include a line of symmetry?

At the end of the session, bring the children back together to compare their symmetrical designs. Favourite ones can be displayed alongside children's accounts of the activity, written using the writing frame on page 128.

DISCUSSION QUESTIONS

- *What will happen if I cut here... or here?*
- *What helps you to predict what the whole design will look like?*
- *Which shapes are easy to create? Which are more difficult?*

ASSESSMENT

Can the children predict what the symmetrical designs will look like? Do they use mathematical language to describe the patterns? Can they follow instructions (see 'Extensions')?

EXTENSIONS

- The children can create their own designs and write instructions for someone else to follow.
- They can fold the paper in half and in half again, then investigate the effects of cutting patterns into the twice-folded piece of paper.
- Photocopiable pages 42 and 43 provide further practice in identifying lines of symmetry and in reflecting shapes, respectively.

SPINNING SHAPES

Whole class, then pairs
50 minutes

AIM

To explore the idea of order of rotational symmetry.

WHAT YOU WILL NEED

Sets of plastic or card 2-D shapes (see list in Glossary, pages 8–9), paper, pencils.

WHAT TO DO

Introduce this activity with a plastic (or card) equilateral triangle on an OHP. Draw round the outline of the shape. Turn the shape slightly to the left or right, so that the children can see it overlapping the outline beneath.

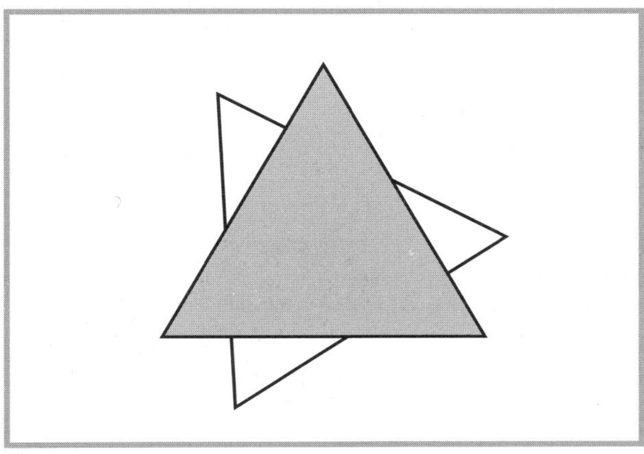

Ask: *What would happen if I kept turning the shape?* Demonstrate that the shape will fit back on itself. *If I carry on turning, what will happen?* Again demonstrate. *Imagine that the triangle is turned around and around – how many different positions will enable it to cover the outline completely?* Explain that this number is called the 'order of rotational symmetry' of the shape. If children are finding it difficult to see this, a good strategy is to mark one corner of the shape; the children can then count the number of different places this mark rests in during the whole rotation.

When you are sure that all the children have understood the idea, repeat with another shape such as an oblong. Draw round it as before, then ask the children to imagine it being turned around. Can they predict how many times it can fit exactly over the outline?

The children should work with a partner, doing the same thing with a variety of shapes: drawing round its outline, predicting the order of its rotational symmetry, then turning it around to check. Afterwards, call the class together to review their findings.

NB Talk about 'turning the shape' (that is, rotating it) rather than 'moving it around', to avoid confusion with translation of the shape.

DISCUSSION QUESTIONS

- *How many times will this shape fit when I turn it around?*
- *Which shapes were easy to predict? Which were trickier?*
- *Do all triangles/quadrilaterals have the same order of rotational symmetry? Why/why not?*

ASSESSMENT

Do the children understand the idea of an order of rotational symmetry? Can they make sensible predictions? Can they draw conclusions from their results?

EXTENSION

The children can design shapes that have a given rotational symmetry.

SLIDING PATTERNS

Whole class, then individuals
50 minutes

AIM

To explore patterns created by translating ('sliding') a shape.

WHAT YOU WILL NEED

A variety of small plastic shapes (thick enough for children to draw round), blank paper, pencils.

WHAT TO DO

This activity is best explained by demonstrating on the board or an OHT. Take a shape and draw round it; carefully slide it to the right; draw round it again; slide it the same distance to the right again; draw around it and so on, several times. Ask the children to describe what you have done, as later you will be expecting them to describe their own patterns. The shapes may fit close together, touch at a point or have a small gap in between, as in the figure opposite (which could be copied onto the board to show the children the different possibilities). You may want to show the class a second example.

The children should individually select a shape (you may want to direct younger or less confident children to the more basic shapes). Stress the need for neatness and accuracy rather than speed. The children should try to continue their pattern across a whole sheet of A4 paper (placed landscape). They should experiment with different kinds of arrangement. On the back of their sheet, they should write a description of how they created the pattern.

The session should conclude with a 'show and tell': each table can nominate one person to show and describe a pattern, or to show the pattern and invite others to describe it. Later, the children can

colour their patterns in alternate colours for artistic effect; the patterns can be mounted and displayed, together with the children's descriptions of them.

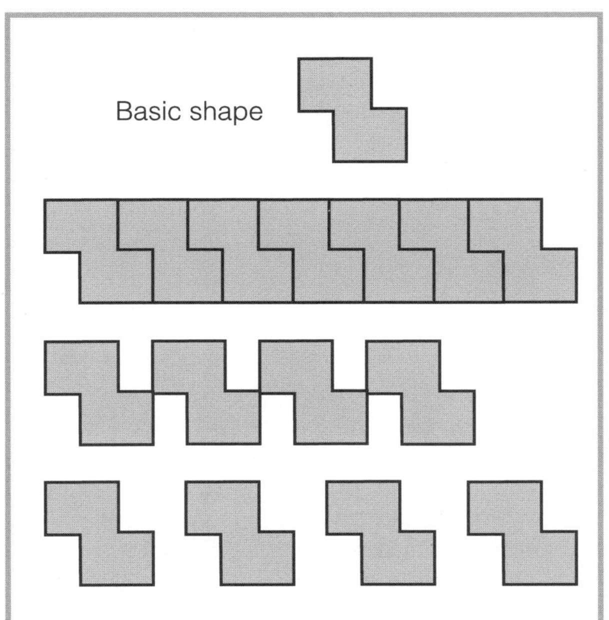

DISCUSSION QUESTIONS

- *How have you moved this shape?*
- *Can you explain this pattern?*

ASSESSMENT

Can the children create a simple sliding pattern? Can they describe their pattern in a way that matches the end result?

EXTENSIONS

- The children can create more complicated patterns by translating the shape vertically as well as horizontally.
- They can go on to 'Change my shape' (page 41), which involves using a computer program to generate patterns.
- Photocopiable page 47 can be used for further practice, or alongside the main activity with some groups. Translating shapes on squared paper can lead to more formal work on co-ordinates with Year 4/Primary 5 pupils; but in this instance the squared grid serves as a guide for accuracy in drawing the shapes.

MIRROR ME

Whole class, then pairs
50 minutes

AIM
To explore vertical and horizontal line symmetry.

WHAT YOU WILL NEED
Small hand mirrors, resource page 122, a set of large capital letters on A4 pages, pencils, pens.

WHAT TO DO
Recap on 'Cut and see' (page 34), in which the children explored simple line symmetry. Tell the children that in this session, they will be using a mirror to explore symmetry in letters. Ask: *Can you think of any capital letters that could be folded down the middle or across the middle to show that they have a line of symmetry?* Write down any suggestions on the board. Hold up large versions of any suggested letters. Ask whether everyone agrees with each suggestion before folding the letter to check.

After establishing a couple of letters (such as A, H or M) that have line symmetry, ask the children to suggest letters that do not. Again, demonstrate to test the suggestions. Note that for some letters (such as A), the line of symmetry is vertical; for others (such as B), it is horizontal. Explain that another way of checking is to use a mirror; demonstrate how to do this.

Now ask the children to pair up. Give each pair an A3 copy of page 122. Next to each letter, they should draw a tick or a cross in pencil to indicate whether it has line symmetry. They should then use a small hand mirror to check their decisions, and go over or correct their original responses with a pen.

When they have all completed the task, bring the class together and discuss their findings (see questions below).

DISCUSSION QUESTIONS
- *How can you tell this letter [A] has symmetry?*
- *Why is this letter [Q] not symmetrical?*
- *Which letters were easy to decide about? Which were harder? Did you get better at deciding?*
- *Which letters have more than one line of symmetry?*

ASSESSMENT
Do the children understand the idea of vertical and horizontal lines of symmetry? Can they make judgements and check them? Can they explain the features that make some letters symmetrical and others not?

VARIATION
- The children can investigate lower-case letters, or the digits 0–9.

EXTENSIONS
- The children can try to create symmetrical words, such as MUM.
- They can use photocopiable pages 42 and 43 to consolidate their understanding of symmetry.
- The activity 'Rotate me' (page 39) explores rotational symmetry of letters in a similar systematic fashion.

ROTATE ME

Whole class, then pairs
50 minutes

AIM
To explore rotational symmetry in letters.

WHAT YOU NEED
Resource page 122, a set of large capital letters on A4 pages, pencils, pens.

WHAT TO DO
Recap on previous activities in which the children have explored aspects of symmetry. In this session, they will be exploring rotational symmetry in letters. Ask the class:

- ***What happens to letters when they are turned around?***
- ***Can you think of any capital letters of the alphabet that, when turned by 90° or 180°, look the same as when upright?***

Write any suggestions on the board and ask whether everyone agrees, then hold up each letter on a sheet of A4 paper and turn it around. After establishing a couple of letters (such as H and I) that have rotational symmetry, ask the children to suggest letters that have no rotational symmetry. Again, demonstrate to confirm or correct the suggestions.

Now ask the children to pair up. Give each pair a copy of page 122. Beside each letter, they should draw a tick or a cross in pencil to indicate whether or not they think the letter has line symmetry. They should then turn the letter to check, and go over or correct their response with a pen.

When they have all completed the task, bring the class back together and discuss their findings.

DISCUSSION QUESTIONS
- ***How can you tell that this letter has/doesn't have rotational symmetry?***
- ***Which letters were easy to predict for? Which were harder?***

ASSESSMENT
Do the children understand the idea of rotational symmetry clearly? Can they make predictions and check them? Can they explain why some letters have rotational symmetry and others do not?

VARIATION
The children can investigate lower-case letters or the digits 0–9.

EXTENSIONS
- The activity 'Mirror me' explores the reflective symmetry of letters in a similar systematic fashion.
- Photocopiable page 44 can be used to check that the children can distinguish between reflective and rotational symmetry.

JOIN UP THE SQUARES

Whole class, then pairs
50 minutes

AIM

To explore the rotational and reflective symmetry of polyominoes.

WHAT YOU WILL NEED

Interlocking squares (such as Polydron or Clixi), a domino, squared paper, pencils.

WHAT TO DO

Explain to the children that a 'polyomino' is a shape made up of squares joined together along one side. Show them a domino: this is the simplest polyomino, since it consists of two squares joined together. Make another 'domino' from two interlocking squares:

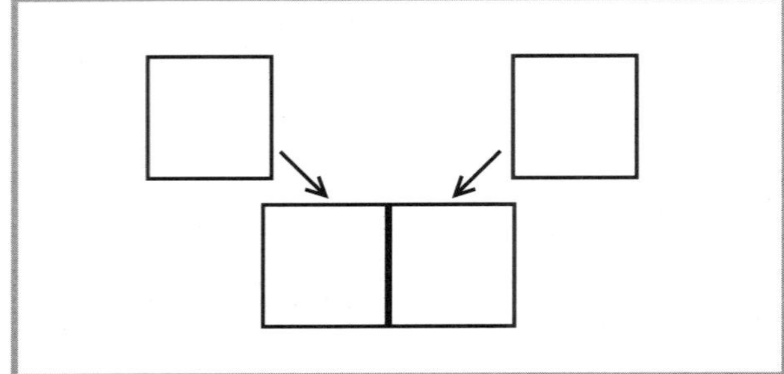

Ask the children to discuss in pairs what a shape made of three interlocking squares might look like. After a few minutes, ask some children to describe the different possible 'triominoes'. As the shapes are described, you should sketch them on the board or make them with the interlocking squares. You need to establish that there are only two unique triominoes (see figure below), though some of the children may describe these in different orientations. Discuss with the children the different reflective and rotational symmetries of each of the two triominoes.

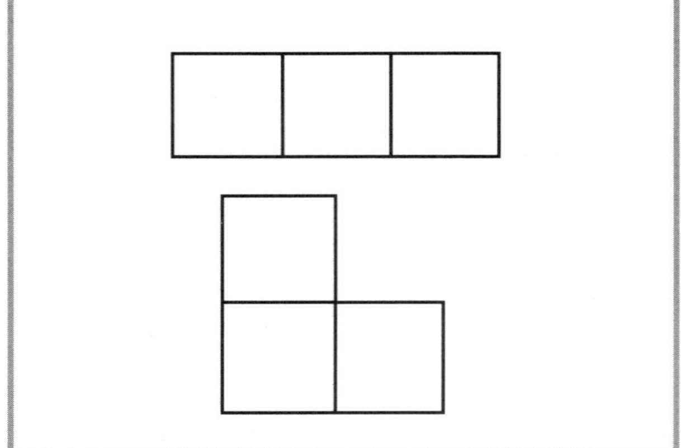

Now set the children the task of working in pairs (or small groups) to make all the different 'tetrominoes' and explore the reflective and rotational symmetries of each. They can use interlocking squares to make the shapes, and also draw their solutions on squared paper (this is useful for tracking the total number of variants).

Bring the class together and ask children to describe the different tetrominoes. For ease of reference, it is useful to establish informal names for them (such as 'the big square' and 'the L'). When all five have been described (see figure below), review the reflective and rotational symmetries of each.

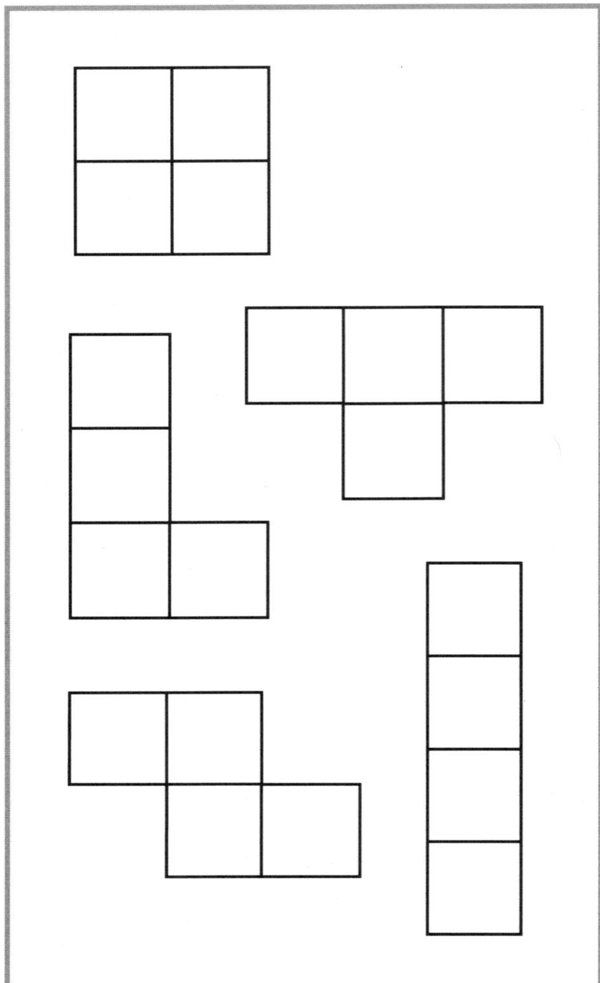

DISCUSSION QUESTIONS

- *Are you sure these two are different?*
- *What happens to that shape when you turn it around/turn it over?*
- *How can you be sure you've found all the solutions?*

ASSESSMENT

Can the children identify the unique tetrominoes, eliminating duplicates that are rotations or reflections of the same arrangement? Can they describe the effect of reflecting and rotating each of the shapes?

VARIATION

- With younger or less confident children, you may prefer to separate the tasks of discovering the five tetrominoes and exploring the rotational and reflective symmetries of each.

EXTENSIONS

- The children can go on to explore pentominoes: combinations of five squares. (There are 12 of these.)
- They can explore combinations of four or five equilateral triangles in the same way.
- Photocopiable pages 45 and 46 provide further practice in reflecting and rotating polyominoes, respectively. The answers for page 45 are: A and G, B and L, C and N, D and E, F and O, J and M, K and P. H and Q have no partner.

With page 46, the children should notice that shapes 3 and 5 have only two unique positions, while all the others have four (in other words, only shapes 3 and 5 have rotational symmetry). Less able children could work with an enlarged version of page 46, using a template and/or a transparent squared grid.

CHANGE MY SHAPE

Paired computer work
15 minutes demonstration, 20 minutes per pair computer time

AIMS

To explore transformations using ICT. To understand the effects of rotation and reflection.

WHAT YOU WILL NEED

A computer graphics program. The effects described below can be generated by almost any computer graphics program; many painting and DTP programs have similar facilities. You might want to provide a list of the specific commands used by the program and instructions for their use. **NB** Some programs use the terms 'turn' and 'flip' instead of 'rotate' and 'reflect', respectively.

WHAT TO DO

Give a short demonstration of the rotation and reflection tools of a computer graphics program. Use a familiar 2-D shape, a piece of clip art or a line of text. It is useful to make a copy of the original shape before transforming it, so that the children can compare it 'before' and 'after'. Ask the children to predict what will happen if, for example, you rotate the shape or reflect it in a horizontal line; then test the predictions.

The children should work at their desks in pairs, looking at different shapes, letters or words and predicting what they will look like when transformed in the following ways:

- reflected horizontally
- reflected vertically
- rotated 90° right or left (a quarter-turn)
- rotated 180° (a half-turn).

They should sketch their predictions, then move to the computer and find out whether they were right. They should create a page showing one or two shapes or designs in a variety of rotations and reflections. Finally, they should print their designs and write (on the computer) about how they were created, giving instructions for someone else to follow.

DISCUSSION QUESTIONS

- *What will happen to that shape when it is reflected?*
- *What will happen to that shape when it is rotated?*
- *How did you make that pattern? Can you write the instructions for someone else to make it?*

ASSESSMENT

Can the children predict the outcomes of various rotations and reflections? Can they use appropriate mathematical language ('reflect' and 'rotate') to describe the effects of the computer program?

EXTENSIONS

- The children can combine two or three different shapes into one design, then use the rotation and reflection tools.
- They can experiment with other facilities of the graphics program to create different effects.

NAME DATE

MARK OF SYMMETRY

■ Mark lines of symmetry on these shapes. Be careful! Some have more than one line of symmetry, and one doesn't have any!

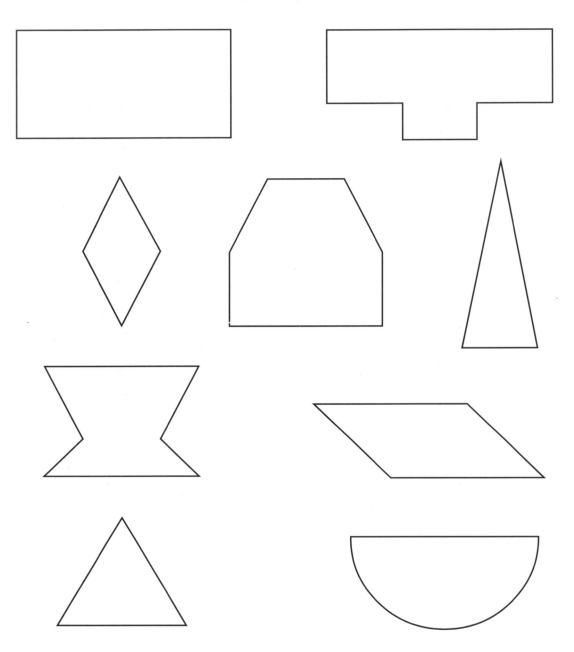

Imagine your friend was absent when your teacher taught you about symmetry. On the back of this sheet, explain it for her using words and pictures.

SEE 'CUT AND SEE', PAGE 34.

NAME DATE

THE OTHER HALF

■ The black line represents a mirror – can you reflect each of the patterns in the mirror line?

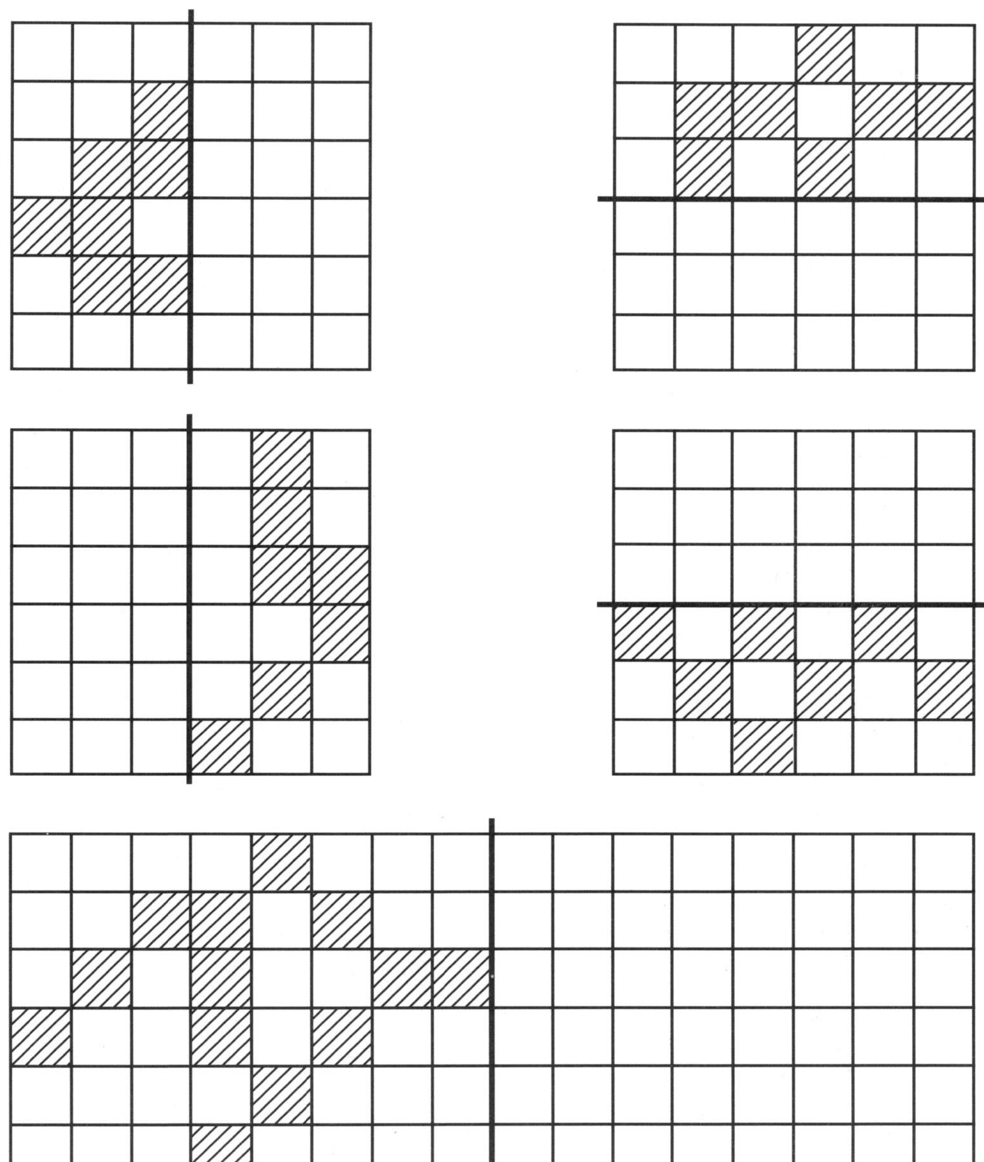

■ Now use squared paper to make up some puzzles like these for your friend to solve.

What makes a good puzzle? What patterns are easy for your friend to complete?

SEE 'CUT AND SEE', PAGE 34.

NAME DATE

TRANSFORMATIONS & SYMMETRY

ROTATE OR REFLECT?

	REFLECTIVE SYMMETRY	NO REFLECTIVE SYMMETRY
ROTATIONAL SYMMETRY	I	S
NO ROTATIONAL SYMMETRY	M	G

- Darren has put these capital letters in the wrong places on the Carroll diagram. Can you help him to move them to the right places?
- Can you find at least one more letter to put in each section?
- Now look at the shapes below and decide where to put them in the diagram.

Check with your partner: do you agree where to put the letters and shapes?

SEE 'ROTATE ME', PAGE 39.

NAME DATE

PAIR THE REFLECTIONS

A B C D

E F G H

J K L M

N O P Q

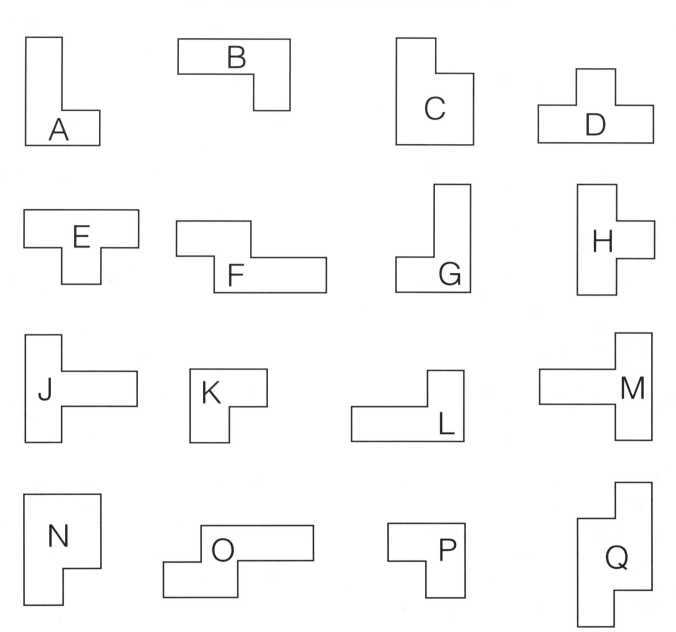

■ Draw lines to join the shapes that are mirror images of each other.

■ Two of the shapes have no partner. Draw them on the back of this sheet, and draw a mirror image beside each one.

Which pairs were the easiest to spot?

SEE 'JOIN UP THE SQUARES', PAGE 40.

NAME DATE

FOLLOW ME AROUND

■ Each of the shapes below has to be rotated, a right angle (quarter-turn) at a time, until it has completed a full turn. The first one has been done for you. Complete the rotations for the other shapes. You can use tracing paper to help!

1

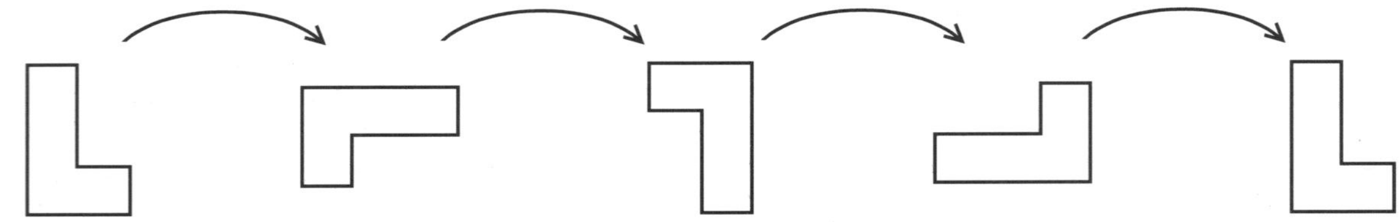

2

3

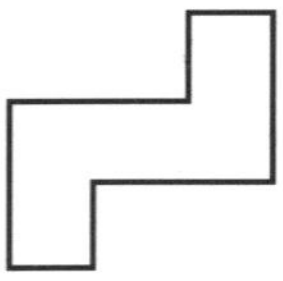

4

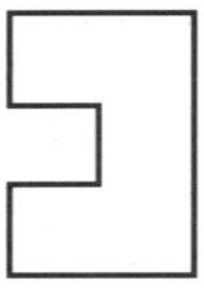

5

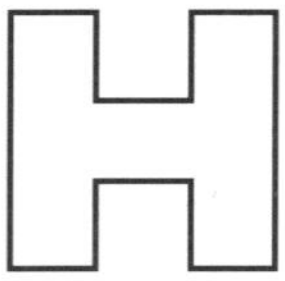

What do you notice about examples 3 and 5 that is different from the others?

Now use the back of the sheet to try rotating some shapes of your own. Look at the effect of rotating them. Which of the examples above are they like?

SEE 'JOIN UP THE SQUARES', PAGE 40.

NAME DATE

SLIDE MY SHAPE

■ Continue to slide these shapes across the grid.

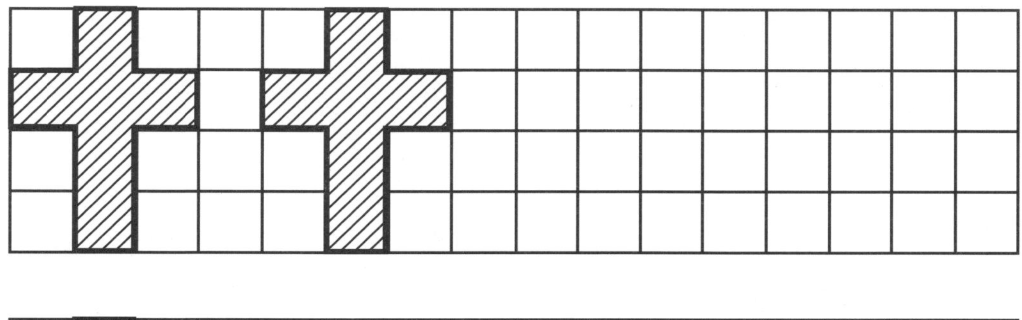

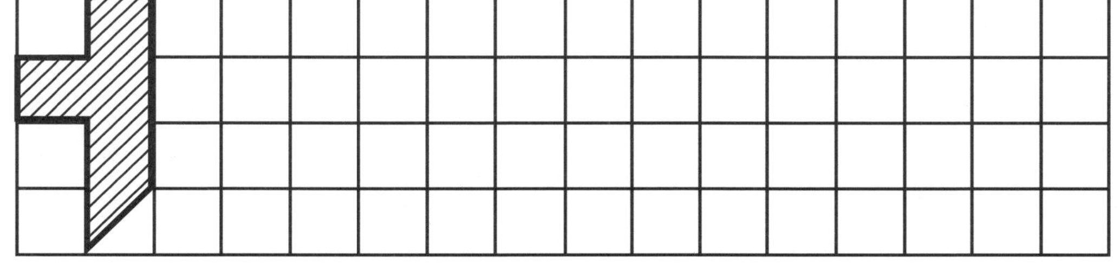

■ Translate this shape horizontally and vertically.

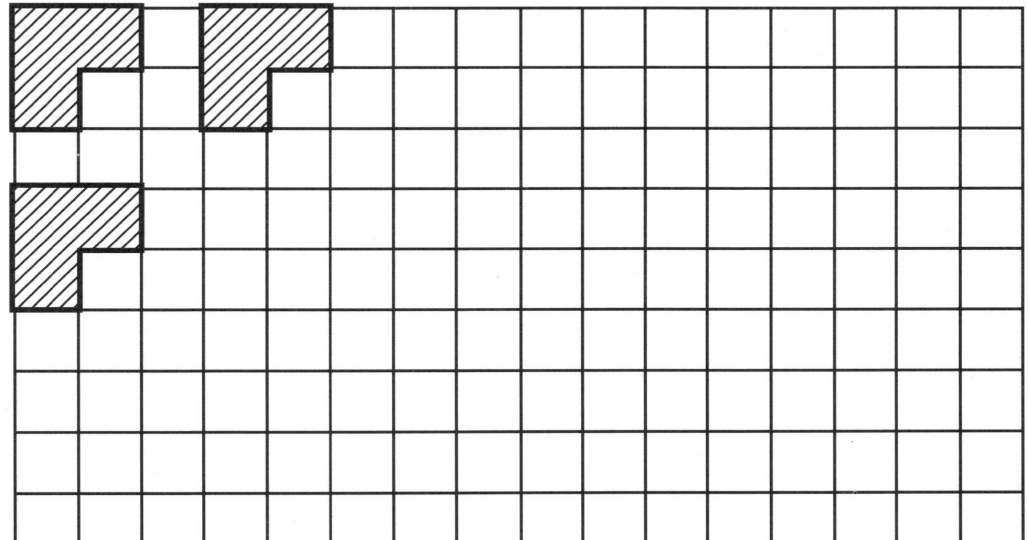

■ Use squared paper to make up some more patterns like these.

Could you do this with plain paper? What would you need to be careful about? Tell your teacher.

SEE 'SLIDING PATTERNS', PAGE 36.

KEY IDEAS

- Following directions (for example, on squared paper or with a floor robot).
- Using the language of position and movement.
- Using compass points (four or eight directions).
- Understanding coordinates (in the first quadrant) and using them for simple shape drawings.

Children's development at this stage should be moving beyond the simple locational language of left, right, above, below, up and down to a mathematical sense of relative position. Thus, in the diagram below, B and C are both to the right of A, but C is four times as far from A as B is. In directing a child to move from A to B or C, therefore, 'move to the right' is not a sufficiently accurate instruction.

A B C

Several activities in this section start with you directing the children (or them directing each other), then go on to situations where the children are directing objects and need to give precise instructions. Encouraging children to participate gives them an opportunity to develop their 'feel' for different directional movements. The use of floor robots is particularly useful in getting children to visualize movements and directions without having to move themselves. This work is useful in preparing children for the use of the LOGO computer environment; more formal work on coordinates will also build on this understanding.

When the children are working with coordinate diagrams, they will need to appreciate the difference between identifying a **square** and identifying a **point**, as illustrated below. Work with these types of grid can be related to the development of map-reading skills, and work using a compass provides further links to geography.

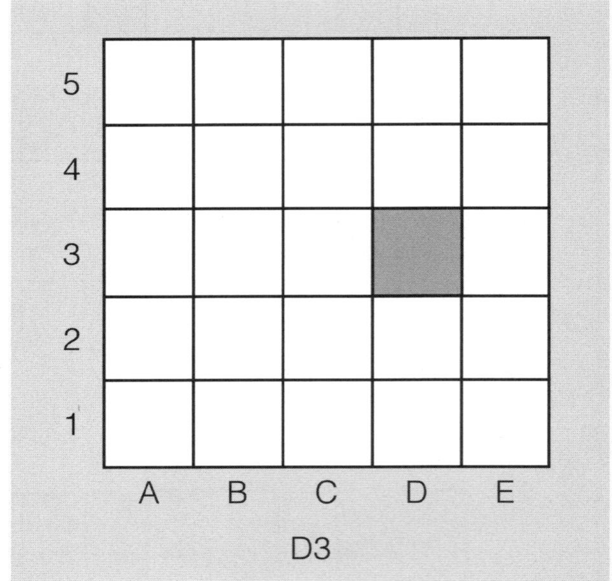

D3

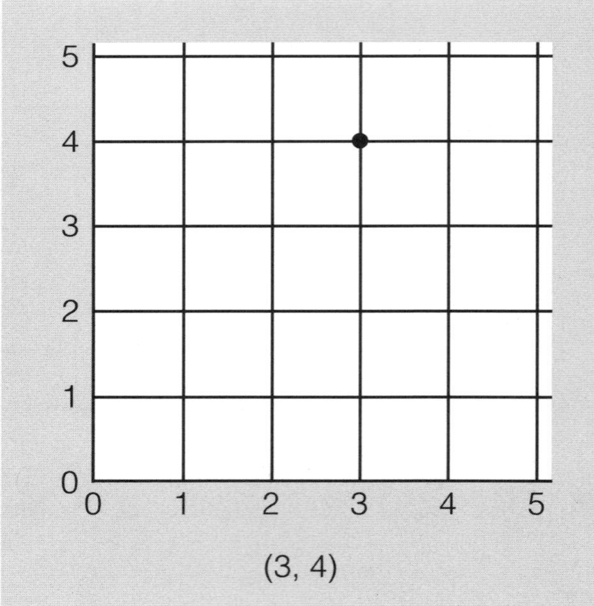

(3, 4)

The ideas of position and direction are crucially about **movement** from one place to another, and work in this section should be linked to the sections on 'Angles' (page 62) and 'Transformation and symmetry' (page 32).

BY THE END OF Y3/P4, MOST CHILDREN SHOULD BE ABLE TO:

- read and begin to write the vocabulary related to position, direction and movement, including turning through right angles (for example, horizontal, vertical, clockwise, anticlockwise)
- describe and find the position of a square on a grid with the rows and columns labelled (eg '3C')
- recognize and use the four compass directions (N, S, E, W).

BY THE END OF Y4/P5, MOST CHILDREN SHOULD BE ABLE TO:

- recognize positions and directions from a description
- describe, and find, the position of a point on a grid of squares where the lines are numbered
- recognize simple examples of horizontal and vertical lines in the environment
- use the eight compass directions (N, S, E, W, NE, NW, SE, SW).

SOME COMMON MISCONCEPTIONS AND STRATEGIES FOR CORRECTING THEM

THIS WAY UP

Confusion is possible when relating objects in different orientations. For example, the phrase 'moving forward' may suggest different things when the children are being directed around a floor maze and when they are using a computer screen or a coordinate diagram: in the former case it may suggest 'moving along', in the latter case 'moving up/down'.

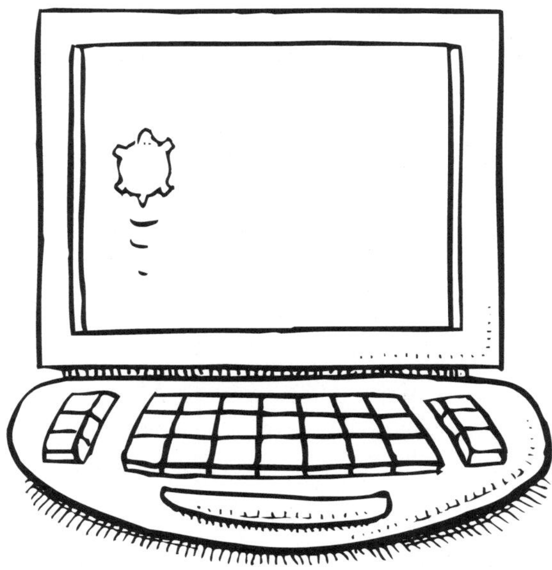

Help the children to see that 'forward' can refer to movement in any direction, perhaps by asking them to imagine themselves on the screen or page.

Getting coordinated

Children often have difficulty in relating a pair of coordinates to a diagram. Which of these points is (2, 4) and which is (4, 2)?

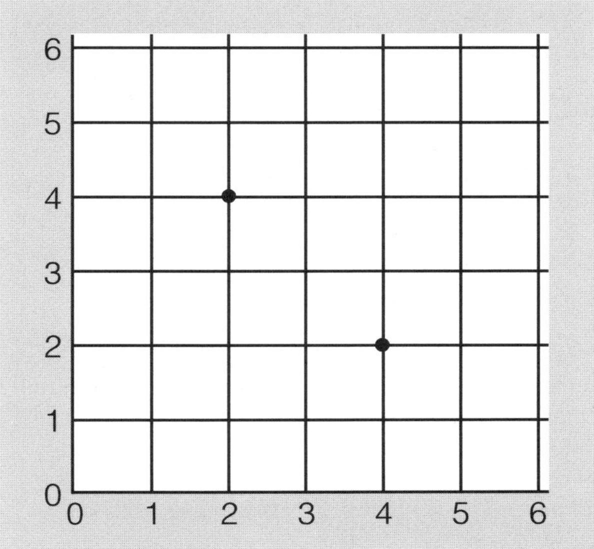

A useful way of remembering the conventional order of coordinates is 'along the hall and up the stairs'.

COMPASS DIRECTIONS

Children often find the order of the four compass directions difficult to remember. Because we tend to speak of 'north, south, east, west', they may put south next to north and east next to west. A mnemonic such as 'No eating soggy waffles' may help, as will reference to world maps where the compass points relate to familiar regions.

DESCRIBE MY SHAPE

Whole class, then pairs
50 minutes

AIM
To develop spatial vocabulary.

WHAT YOU WILL NEED
Cards showing the words: **horizontal, vertical, diagonal, left, right, top, bottom, above, below, halfway**; paper, card.

WHAT TO DO
Attach the vocabulary cards to the board. Draw the shape shown below on the board, and ask the children to copy it. Ask them to consider how they might tell a friend how to draw this shape over the telephone. Draw attention to the words you want them to use.

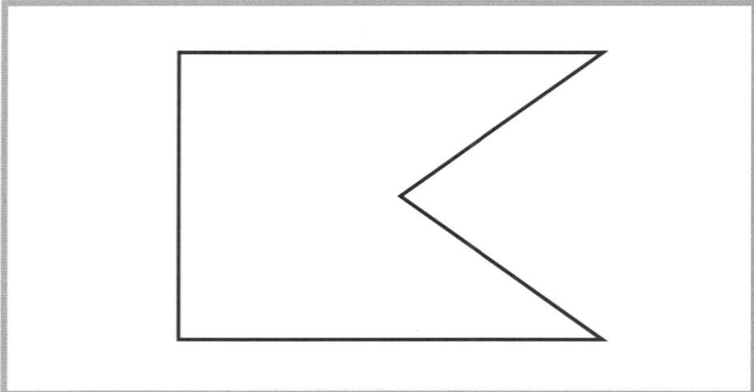

Children may find this difficult to begin with, so be prepared to model it for them: read out the following instructions, asking the children to draw the shape as you speak. (Less able children could copy the shape and trace around it as you speak.) *Starting at the bottom left-hand corner, draw a horizontal line to the right. Then go diagonally up to the left until you are above the halfway mark on the original line. Then turn and go diagonally up to the right until you are at the top right-hand corner. Then go horizontally to the left until you are above the point you started from. Now drop straight down to that point, drawing a vertical line.*

Ask for a volunteer to repeat the instructions, or to give another set of instructions starting from a different point on the shape.

Now ask the children to invent their own shapes. To begin with, it is a good idea to restrict the number of sides (say, to eight) and to stick to straight lines. As they become more confident, the restrictions can be dropped. They should draw a shape of their own and write a description of it, using the key positional vocabulary on the cards. They should then read their descriptions to a partner, see whether he or she can follow their instructions, and amend the instructions if necessary. Emphasize that this is a co-operative activity: the aim is to help each other write unambiguous instructions, not to catch each other out.

In the Plenary session, bring the class together; ask some children to show and describe their shapes, and to reflect on the vocabulary used. Ask one or two children to read out their instructions to see whether the whole class can draw their shapes. The children could also cut their shapes from card, making a class collection of shapes that can be used again for this activity.

DISCUSSION QUESTIONS
- *What shapes have you found easy/difficult to follow instructions for?*
- *What words help with the description?*

ASSESSMENT
Can the children give unambiguous instructions for drawing their shapes? Do they use the spatial vocabulary appropriately?

EXTENSION
When the children are confident, they can try the activity in pairs with a screen between them: one child gives instructions for the other to recreate the shape.

GRID GAMES

Whole class
50 minutes

AIM
To use an alphanumeric grid diagram (with labelled squares).

WHAT YOU WILL NEED
The hall or playground, chalk. Draw the diagram below on the floor (there may already be some permanent grid lines that can be included, perhaps as the horizontal and vertical axes). Each cell should be large enough for a child to stand clearly inside.

WHAT TO DO
Start by quickly calling out children's names and directing each child to a cell (for example: *Iqbal, C2; Karen, D3*). If necessary, demonstrate how to find the cell by locating the horizontal coordinate, then moving up to find the vertical one. After all the children have been placed, ask them to direct each other to particular cells in the same way.

Now ask one child to go to a particular cell, then ask the class to imagine this child moving in a particular way – for example: 2 up, 2 down, 3 left or 3 right. When they are confident with this, try combining instructions: *If Sam moves 3 right and 1 back, where will she be?* A possible variation is to direct two children to different cells, then ask the rest of the class what movement one child will have to make to reach the other.

This activity can be repeated using four-point compass directions. Draw a large compass next to the grid, with 'up' being nominally north (see illustration). Explain that the real compass directions are fixed. Give instructions such as: *Move 2 squares east; Move 3 squares north.*

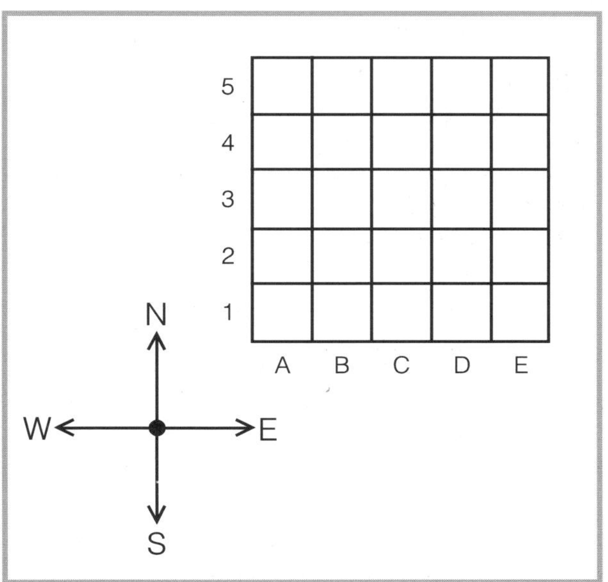

DISCUSSION QUESTIONS
- *If you move 2/3/4 squares left, where will you end up?*
- *Which square will Clare move to?*

ASSESSMENT
Do the children understand how the coordinate diagram works? Can they follow instructions? Can they describe movements from place to place on the coordinate diagram? Do they use the four compass directions confidently?

EXTENSIONS
- Extend the grid to 8 × 8 as the children become more confident.
- Introduce diagonal movements.
- The children can move a floor robot around a similar grid (make the cell measurements equivalent to the length of the robot).
- Photocopiable pages 56 and 57 can be used for follow-up classroom work on alphanumeric coordinates. Page 56 focuses on naming grid squares with coordinates. Page 57 (you will need two copies for each child) involves giving coordinates as instructions.

FIND THE PLACE

Whole class
20 minutes (repeat several times)

AIM
To use a numerical coordinate grid.

WHAT YOU WILL NEED
A large diagram of a coordinate grid (see below), drawn on the board or an acetate. You can make an acetate from photocopiable page 59.

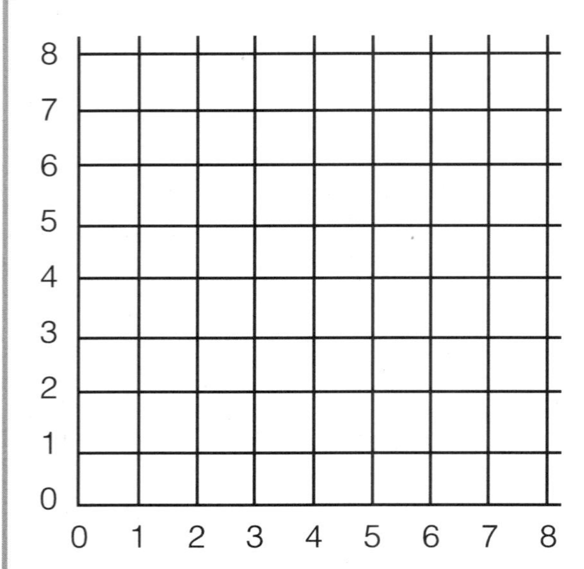

WHAT TO DO
Display the coordinate diagram and explain how it works. Point out the difference from the square grid used in 'Grid games' (page 51): the coordinates refer to the points where lines intersect, not to squares. As with the square grid, the horizontal coordinate is read first in each pair: to find the point (3, 4), move 3 horizontally and then 4 vertically. The brackets are another convention that the children should be encouraged to use.

Use the large coordinate diagram for various introductory activities, such as two or three of the following:

1. Mark a random selection of points (A–M) on the grid, then choose points at random and ask children to tell you what their coordinates are. Ask the rest of the class whether they agree.
2. As 1, but this time call out the coordinates; the children have to say what letter is marked at each point.
3. Use a blank grid. Call up a child to mark on a particular point such as (2, 6). Ask the class whether it has been placed correctly. Now call up a second child and ask the first child to give the second child a coordinate pair to place. Then the second child sets coordinates for the third, and so on until they have all had a turn.
4. Mark one point on the grid, such as (2, 3). Tell the children that this is one corner of a square. Ask them to suggest what the coordinates of the other three corners might be. Repeat for a range of other shapes (such as an oblong and various triangles), or for some capital letters (such as E, T and X).

DISCUSSION QUESTIONS
- *How can you remember which number comes first?*
- *What is the difference between (3, 4) and (4, 3)?*
- *What do you notice about the points (2, 1) (2, 2) (2, 3) (2, 4)? What about (1, 3) (2, 3) (3, 3) (3, 4)?*
- *How can you tell when four coordinate points will make a square?*

ASSESSMENT
Can the children give the coordinates of points marked on a grid? Can they find points on the grid from coordinate pairs? Can they distinguish the point (3, 4) from the point (4, 3)?

EXTENSIONS
- Extend the grid to 10 × 10 or 12 × 12 as the children become more confident.
- Photocopiable pages 58 and 59 provide similar activities for individual practice. The answers for page 58 are: A (1, 2) (5, 2) (5, 5) (1, 5); B (2, 1) (5, 1) (5, 4) (2, 4); C (1, 2) (3, 1) (5, 4) (3, 5); D (2, 2) (4, 2) (5, 3) (5, 4) (4, 5) (2, 5) (1, 4) (1, 3).

MAKE MY TANGRAM

Whole class, then pairs
50 minutes

AIMS
To consolidate the names of 2-D shapes. To use positional language (see below).

WHAT YOU WILL NEED
Tangram sets (made by photocopying resource page 125 onto card); tangram pictures (use the examples on page 125, or any others the children have created); a large book (such as an atlas) for each pair of children. This activity requires the children to be familiar with the classic tangram set (see the '2-D and 3-D shapes' section, page 22).

WHAT TO DO
This activity is best explained through demonstration. If possible, projecting the shadows of the pieces on an OHP will be very effective. Model how to give instructions to recreate one of the tangram designs. Suitable phrases might include: *Take the largest triangle. Place the square on its side on top of the triangle. Put the smallest triangle to the left of the square. Place the parallelogram beside the small triangle, matching the long sides.*

The children should work in pairs, using a large book as a screen (see illustration): one child giving instructions to make a tangram design, the other trying to make it. Circulate around the class, checking especially that the children are working co-operatively. Emphasize that with good instructions, the partner should be able to recreate the pattern; the purpose is not to catch your partner out.

After the children have made several attempts each, bring them together to discuss their work.

DISCUSSION QUESTIONS
- *Which tangram designs were easier/harder to recreate?*
- *Were the directions easy or hard to follow?*
- *What helped to make them easy to follow?*
- *Were some tangram pieces easier to use than others?*

ASSESSMENT
Can the children give unambiguous instructions? Can they recreate their partner's tangram design?

VARIATION
The children can work in groups of three or four, with one child giving directions to the others. This will allow them to compare interpretations of a single set of instructions.

POSITION & DIRECTION

FROM START TO FINISH

Whole class, then pairs
50 minutes

AIMS

To describe movements using directional vocabulary. To follow a sequence of instructions.

WHAT YOU WILL NEED

A variety of obstacles (benches, chairs, mats, rounders posts and so on), blindfolds, paper, pencils.

WHAT TO DO

Set up a range of obstacles around the hall (vary the number of these according to the children's experience with this type of activity). Mark two or three small areas (for example, corners of the hall, the centre circle) as designated 'Start' spots, and another two or three small areas as designated 'Finish' spots.

Ask for a volunteer and put him or her at one of the 'Start' points, blindfolded. Now ask the other children to give that child directions in order to guide him or her towards a 'Finish' point. You may want to rehearse some appropriate language first – for example: **forward, backward, steps, turn right, turn left, stop.**

When the child has completed the route, remove the blindfold and ask him or her to report back on what instructions were helpful. One thing that will need some discussion is the length of a 'step'. You may want to repeat this activity a couple of times, using different start and finish points, before moving on to the next task.

Now sort the class into groups of four to six, and give each group a different 'Start' and 'Finish' point. Working in pairs within the group, they should write instructions for a route between these points. They should then try out the different routes, see whether they all work, and agree on which route is the most efficient. When several groups are trying out routes simultaneously, it may be better not to use blindfolds.

When they have spent some time practising their solutions, stop the class and allow the groups to demonstrate their routes (you may even volunteer to be directed around the hall yourself). Finish with some discussion about the language used and the efficiency of the solutions.

DISCUSSION QUESTIONS

- *What is the best way to go from here to there?*
- *What instructions were easy to follow?*
- *How could we move the obstacles to make this task easier/harder to complete? (See 'Variation'.)*

ASSESSMENT

Can the children follow instructions? Can they create a set of unambiguous instructions? Can they refine their instructions to make the routes more efficient?

VARIATION

Give the children an opportunity to rearrange the obstacles. Can they make the task of moving from A to B a lot more complicated?

EXTENSION

The children can create a smaller obstacle course, then give a floor robot instructions to navigate it.

MAYBE I'M A MAZE

Whole class, then pairs
50 minutes

AIMS
To describe movements using directional vocabulary. To follow a sequence of instructions.

WHAT YOU WILL NEED
Resource page 126 (one copy per pair, or as OHT), squared paper, rulers, pencils, counters (optional).

WHAT TO DO
Start by rehearsing some of the language the children will need, such as: **up one square, down two squares, left, right, back, along**.

Then ask the children to consider the two mazes on page 126. How can they describe the route from the IN square to the OUT square in each case? One child should put his or her finger (or a counter) at the start point, and the partner should give directions for the first child to follow. Alternatively, if you have made an OHT of the mazes, you can ask the children to give you directions as you follow the route. Let the children take turns to do this.

Now distribute sheets of squared paper and set children the task of designing their own maze. They should use only horizontal and vertical lines, as in the examples, and write a set of instructions to guide their partner through the maze. They should then swap mazes and try to follow each other's directions.

Finally, share some of the children's mazes with the class by copying them onto the board or an OHT. You may want to collect some of the best examples together for a class book or wall display.

DISCUSSION QUESTIONS
- *What is the best route through the maze?*
- *How can you describe the route?*
- *What happens to the instructions if you go backwards, from the finish to the start?*

ASSESSMENT
Can the children follow directions to go through the maze? Can they create a set of unambiguous instructions for getting through a maze? How complex are their own maze designs?

VARIATION
Draw a four-point compass beside each maze on page 126 and ask the children to use north, south, east and west in their instructions.

EXTENSIONS
- The children can work with mazes that do not have a simple horizontal and vertical line format (there are many books with examples).
- They can create a small maze (using metre sticks, rulers, building bricks and so on) to move a floor robot around.
- Copy the mazes on page 126 onto separate acetates and stick them over a computer screen (enlarge each maze so that it covers the screen). Ask the children to use a LOGO program to move through each maze. Further instructions on using LOGO can be found in the companion Scholastic book *Developing Shape, Space and Measures with 9–11 year olds.*
- Photocopiable pages 60 and 61 provide further maze activities (involving giving and following directions) for pairs to attempt.

NAME DATE

POSITION & DIRECTION

WHICH SQUARES?

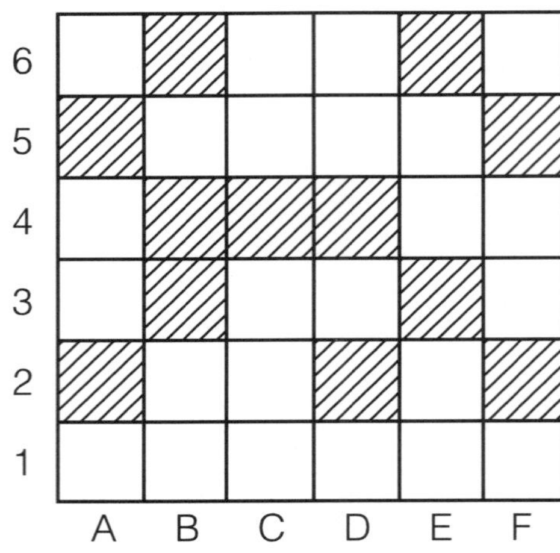

■ Write down the coordinates of the 12 shaded squares:

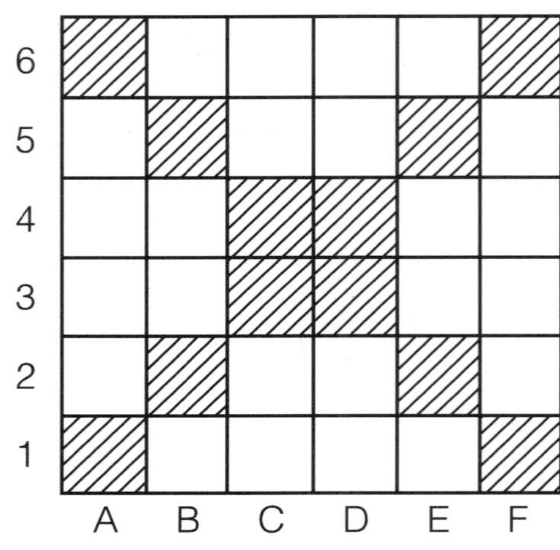

■ Write down the coordinates of the 12 shaded squares:

On the back of the sheet write some instructions for a friend, explaining how to find the coordinates for any shaded square.

SEE 'GRID GAMES', PAGE 51.

NAME DATE

PLAN A PATTERN

■ Use the grids below to design patterns of your own. Make a note of the coordinates for each pattern in the space below it.

■ Now write down the coordinates of your two patterns on a separate piece of paper. Give them to a friend – can he or she recreate your patterns on another copy of this sheet?

Pattern A

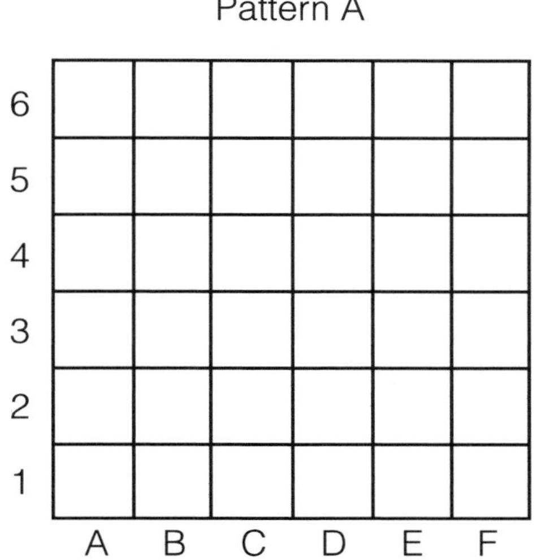

Coordinates for Pattern A:

Pattern B

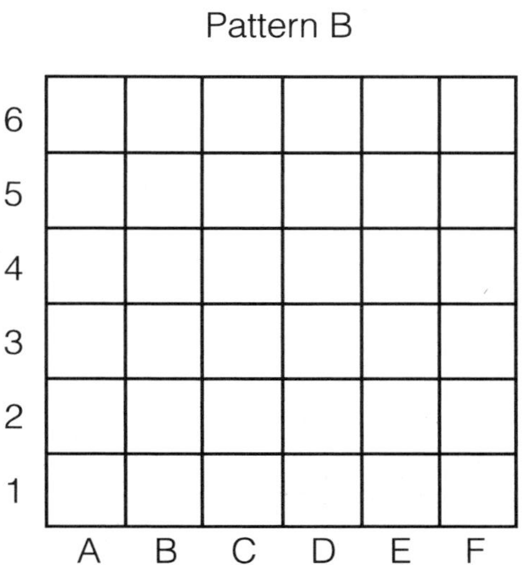

Coordinates for Pattern B:

What is the most important thing to remember when giving or following these instructions?

SEE 'GRID GAMES', PAGE 51.

NAME DATE

FIND THE POINTS

■ Write down the coordinates for each of these shapes:

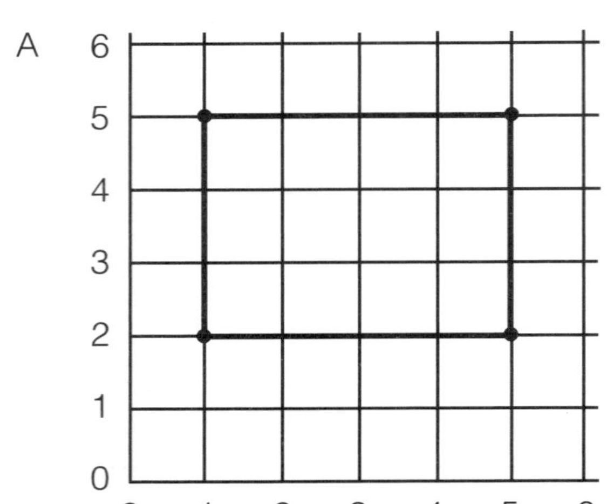

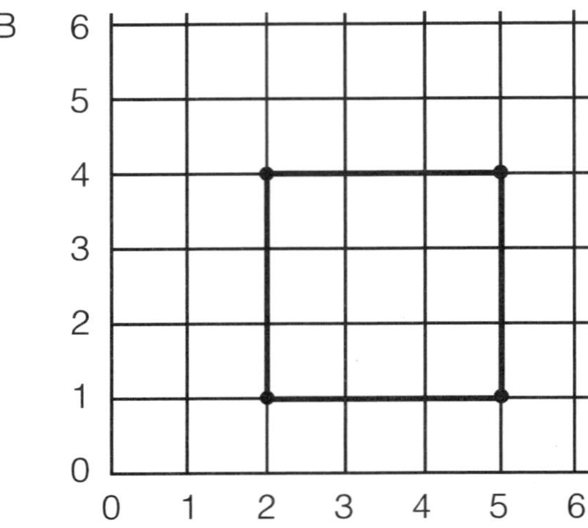

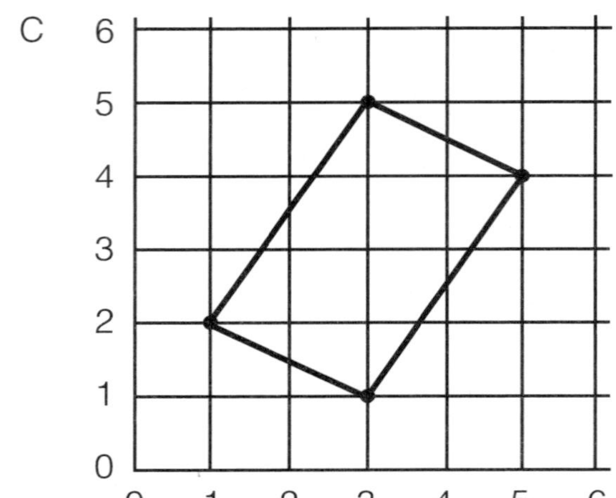

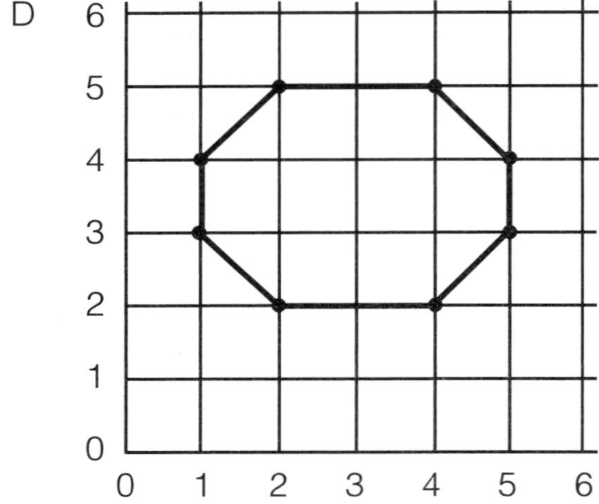

On the back of the sheet write some instructions for a friend who has been away from school, explaining how to find the coordinates from the shapes on the grid.

SEE 'FIND THE PLACE', PAGE 52.

POSITION & DIRECTION

NAME DATE

MAKE A SHAPE

■ Plot points on the diagram below and join them to show: **1)** a square, **2)** an oblong, **3)** a different oblong, **4)** a triangle, **5)** a shape with more than four sides. Use a different colour for each shape.

■ Write the coordinates for each shape here:

Square ______________________________

First oblong ______________________________

Second oblong ______________________________

Triangle ______________________________

Shape with more than four sides ______________________________

____

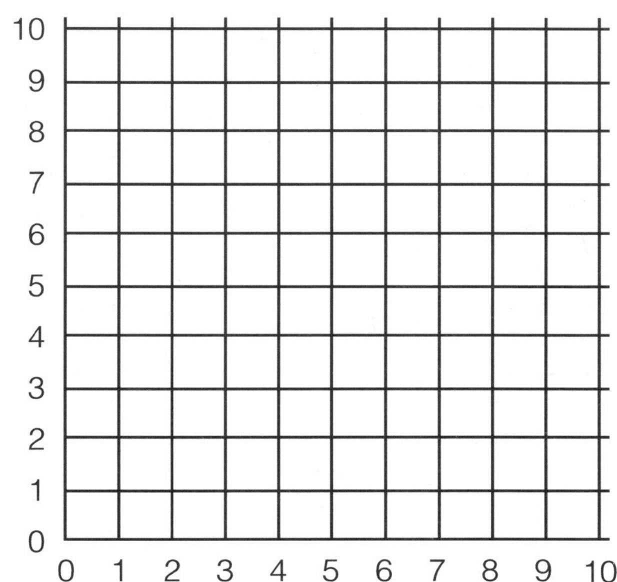

■ Check your coordinates for each shape. When you are sure they are correct, copy them onto another page for a friend to try.

Which coordinates do you think will be hardest for your friend to plot?

SEE 'FIND THE PLACE', PAGE 52.

NAME DATE

GET ME OUT OF HERE

■ Next to each of these mazes, write the instructions to get from the start to the finish.

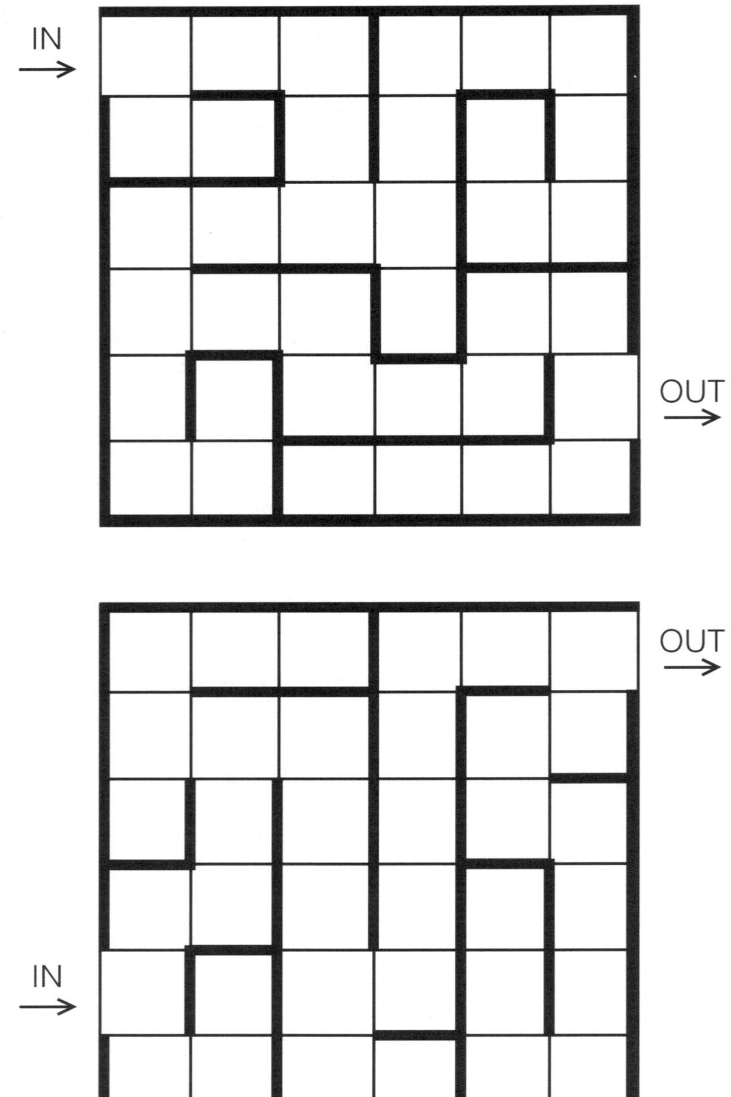

Compare your instructions with your friend's. Did you both use the same route to get through the maze?

Use squared paper to draw your own maze design. Write instructions for getting through the maze.

SEE 'MAYBE I'M A MAZE', PAGE 55.

NAME DATE

MOUSE MAZE

■ This maze has several dead ends where cheese is hidden. Write down the four routes from the entrance to the points A, B, C and D.

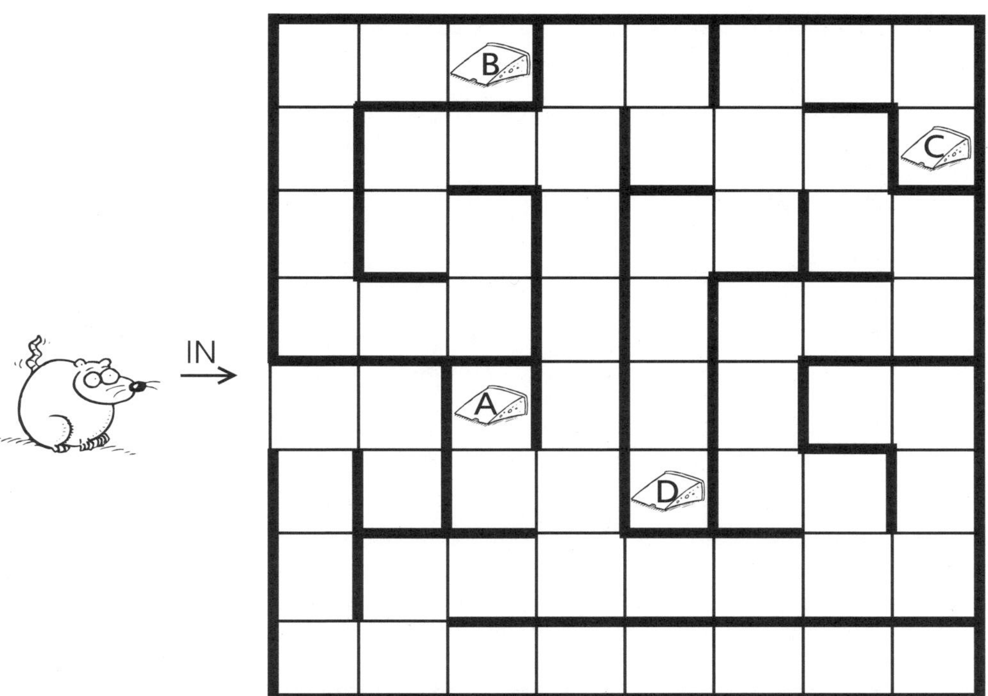

How to get to A: ______

How to get to B: ______

How to get to C: ______

How to get to D: ______

■ Now cut out your route instructions, mix them up and give them to a friend. Can your friend work out which store of cheese each of your instructions leads to?

SEE 'MAYBE I'M A MAZE', PAGE 55.

KEY IDEAS

- Understanding that angle is a measure of turn.
- Using angle to describe the 'shape' of a corner.
- Developing a sense of the relative size of angles.
- Understanding clearly what a right angle represents.
- Becoming aware of 60° and 45° angles.
- Recognizing different angles in the environment.
- Investigating angles in the context of familiar images, particularly a clock face and a compass.

Children's developing awareness of angle at this age is linked closely to that of **rotational direction**, and to a description of a shape's properties.

Rotational direction is linked to the notion of angle as a measure of turn. In this section, there are activities that involve movement around a clock face or a compass. Turning can be described as either 'clockwise' (or 'turning to the right') or 'anti-clockwise' (or 'a turn to the left').

Turning 'all the way around' prepares children for an understanding that a 'whole turn' is equivalent to 360° and a 'quarter-turn' is therefore equivalent to 90° (a right angle). Turning themselves or a floor robot helps children to remember these facts, and is an important prerequisite for more formal pencil and paper activities.

Within the context of angle, children should also develop appropriate vocabulary for describing shapes. At the beginning of Year 3/Primary 4, children will be used to describing shapes in terms of the relative length of sides (for example, 'a square has four sides the same length'). Descriptions of shapes in terms of angle (for example, 'a square has four right angles') are more subtle, because they are not always as easy to see. In this context, angle is being used in a static sense: to describe the shape of the corner. Is it a right angle, or less than, or more than a right angle? By the end of Year 4/Primary 5, children may be ready to start using 'acute' and 'obtuse' to describe these aspects.

BY THE END OF Y3/P4, MOST CHILDREN SHOULD BE ABLE TO:

- make and describe right-angled turns, including turns between the four compass points (some children will know that a right angle is 90°)
- identify right angles in 2-D shapes and in the environment
- recognize that a straight line is equivalent to two right angles (some children will know that this is 180°)
- compare other angles with a right angle.

BY THE END OF Y4/P5, MOST CHILDREN SHOULD BE ABLE TO:

- make and measure clockwise and anti-clockwise turns
- know that angles are measured in degrees, that one whole turn is 360° or four right angles, and hence that a quarter-turn is 90° or one right angle
- start to order a set of angles each less than 180° (some children will be able to identify angles as 'acute' or 'obtuse').

SOME COMMON MISCONCEPTIONS AND STRATEGIES FOR CORRECTING THEM

BIGGER ANGLES

In talking about the 'size' of an angle, children may confuse the amount of turn with the length of the 'arms'. Is the second of these two angles bigger than the first?

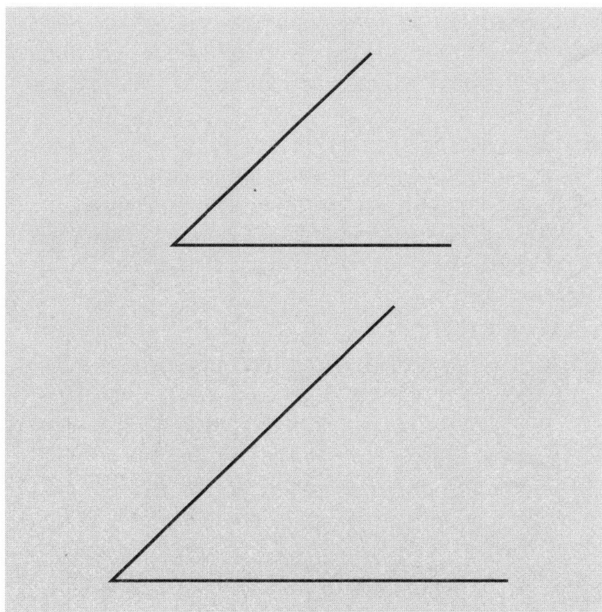

Both of these angles are of course the same size. This can be demonstrated by placing a tracing or acetate of one over the other.

'LEFT ANGLES'

Children may refer to the figure on the left as a 'left angle':

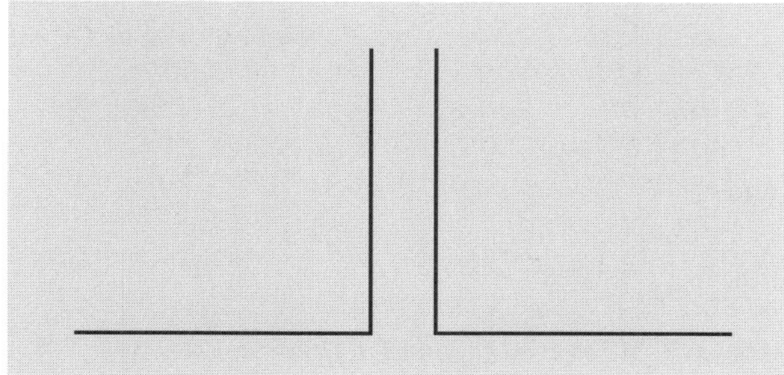

Explain that the term 'right angle' has nothing to do with right and left: it comes from building and joining, where a 90° angle (as between horizontal and vertical) is referred to as a 'true' or 'right' angle.

ANGLES IN DIFFERENT ORIENTATIONS

Children may have difficulty in recognizing angles in 'odd' orientations, as with shape recognition (see the '2-D and 3-D shapes' section, page 11). All of the angles below are right angles:

Make sure that the children see and use angles (initially right angles) in a variety of situations and orientations.

DIFFERENT DEGREES

Children may confuse 'degrees' as a measure of angle with 'degrees' as a measure of temperature. Explain that 'degree' is not a physical unit like 'gram' or 'metre', but a word meaning 'amount'. A temperature is measured in degrees Celsius. A degree of turn is simply a measure of a certain angle or proportion of turn.

HUNT THE RIGHT ANGLES

Whole class
50 minutes

AIM
To identify right angles and angles greater or less than right angles.

WHAT YOU WILL NEED
Roughly torn scrap paper, plastic 2-D and 3-D shapes, a variety of small objects, pencils, paper.

WHAT TO DO
Give each child a piece of scrap paper – the demonstration will be even more effective if the piece of paper is torn and tattered around the edges. Ask the children to fold the paper roughly in half, making sure that the edge is very firm. Now they should make a second fold, very firmly, across the first (see illustration). They should all have made a right angle. Check whether they know what the angle is called. Ask them to close their eyes and run a finger around it: they should feel the two smooth edges and the 'point' at the corner. Ask someone to describe this.

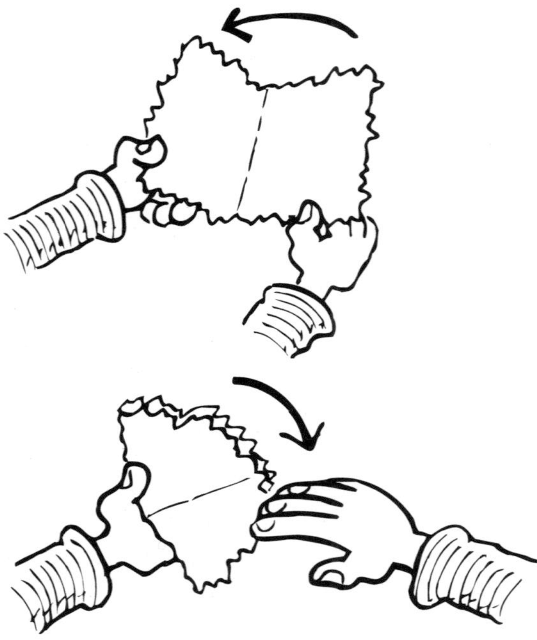

Now ask the children to suggest where in the classroom they can find right angles (corners of desks and books, window and door frames, and so on). They should now 'hunt for right angles' around the classroom and make a note of all the ones they find. Demonstrate how to check for right angles by holding the home-made right angle over a suspected right angle.

Call the class together and discuss their findings. Now tell the children that not all angles are right angles: some are greater, some less. Demonstrate this using shapes with a range of angles (such as a triangle with an obtuse angle). Show how, by carefully placing one edge of their right angle over one side of the shape and lining up the corners, they can find out whether any angle is greater or less than a right angle:

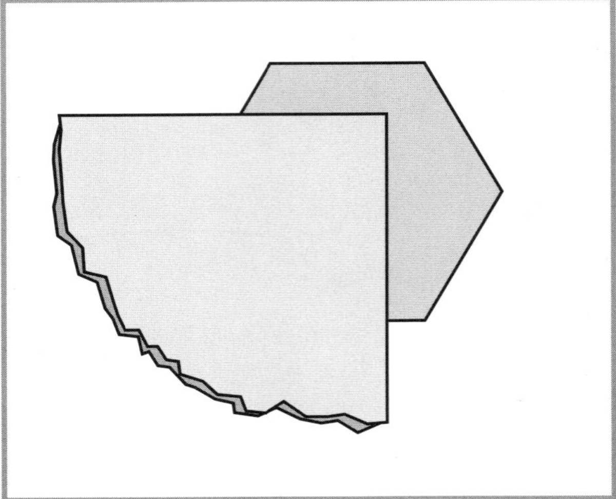

Distribute a range of plastic shapes and other objects, and ask the children to investigate the angles of each object to determine which have angles greater or less than right angles (as well as further examples of right angles). Again, call the children together to discuss their findings.

DISCUSSION QUESTIONS
- *Can you describe how your right angle feels?*
- *How can you be sure this angle is a right angle?*
- *Which of these angles are more than a right angle? Which are less? How do you know?*

ASSESSMENT
Can the children describe the characteristics of a right angle? Can they determine whether or not shapes have right angles, angles greater than right angles or angles less than right angles?

VARIATION
- The children can look for right angles in the hall or playground.

EXTENSIONS
- The children can use the writing frame on photocopiable page 128 to describe what they have done.
- Photocopiable page 70, 71 and 72 all provide further practice in this topic. Page 70 involves comparing and ordering angles by size; page 71 involves comparing angles in various shapes; page 72 extends this to drawing shapes with given angle properties, and includes reference to 90° angles.

MOVING ARMS

Whole class
30 minutes

AIMS
To understand angle as a measure of turn. To get a 'feel' for different angles in a practical context.

WHAT YOU WILL NEED
Geostrips (commercially available, or made from resource page 127 copied onto card and covered with sticky-backed plastic), split-pin paper fasteners, felt-tipped pens, paper right angles (see 'Hunt the right angles', page 64). Each child will need two geostrips.

WHAT TO DO
Talk to the children about how angle is a measure of turn. Give a few practical demonstrations such as opening and closing a door or window and moving the thumb and first finger together, then apart.

Show the children how to join two geostrips together. They should mark the tips of the geostrips 1 and 2. Ask them to make a right angle, and then to move geostrip 1 over the top of geostrip 2. Explain that this turn is equal to the angle, and that turning a geostrip by a right angle is called a '90° turn'. Ask: *Why 90°?* Place one geostrip over the other and turn it around by a full circle (keeping the other geostrip fixed). Ask the children to do this. Explain that a full circle is divided into 360 degrees (a measure devised by the ancient Babylonians), and a right angle is a quarter of this. Use four paper right angles from 'Hunt the right angles' (page 64) to show how four right angles make a full turn. This also explains why a right angle is referred to as a quarter turn (see illustration).

Give the children some time to play with their geostrip pairs, making angles of less than 90° and greater than 90°. Finish by asking them to describe the movement needed to make each type of angle.

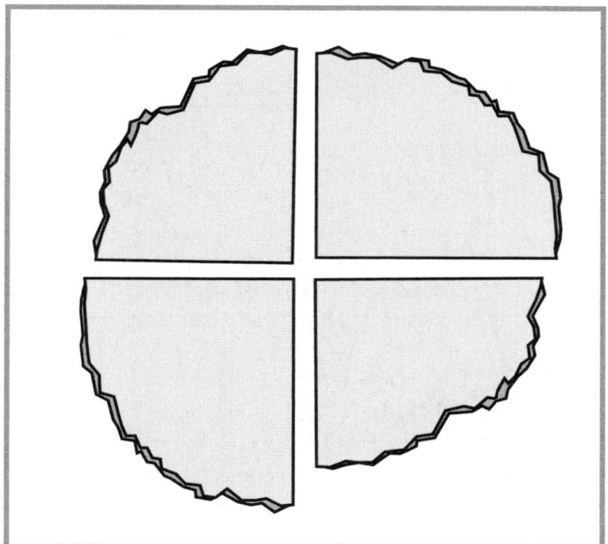

DISCUSSION QUESTIONS
- *What other things turn like this?*
- *What angle is a full turn?*
- *Who can describe a right angle as an amount of turn?*

ASSESSMENT
Can the children describe angles in terms of amount of turn? Do they understand how to make a right angle using the geostrips?

EXTENSIONS
- The children can use their geostrip pairs to recreate movements around a compass or a clock face when they are working on photocopiable pages 74 and 75 respectively.

TURN AROUND

Whole class
50 minutes

AIM
To understand the effect of different amounts and directions of turn.

WHAT YOU WILL NEED
The school hall.

WHAT TO DO
Play the following as a 'Simon says' game (any instruction prefaced by 'Simon says' should be obeyed, all others should be ignored). The children should all face you to begin with. Check that they are sure about the following directions: right and left (wave hands); clockwise and anti-clockwise; a quarter-turn, half-turn and whole turn. (When demonstrating left and right, stand with your back to the children so that your left is also theirs.)

The instructions should combine a fraction with a direction – for example: *Simon says do a quarter-turn left; Simon says do a whole turn clockwise; Simon says do a half-turn right.* Explain the game by demonstrating. Each turn should begin where the previous one left off – for example, a quarter-turn right followed by a half-turn left followed by a quarter-turn clockwise leaves you facing in the direction you started with.

After playing the game for some time, ask for a volunteer (choose someone who has been good at following the instructions). Now ask several children to give this child instructions (as in the game). Before the volunteer moves, ask the class to predict each time which direction he or she will be facing when the move is completed.

DISCUSSION QUESTIONS
- ***Which are the easiest/hardest instructions to follow?***
- ***What happens if two people start off facing each other, then one does a half-turn left and the other does a half-turn right?***
- ***What move would result in the opposite of a quarter-turn left?***

ASSESSMENT
Can the children follow the instructions? Can they predict the effect of different amounts and directions of turn?

VARIATIONS
- The children can play in pairs: one giving the instructions, the other carrying them out and the first checking.
- Increase the difficulty of the instructions by including three-quarter turns, a turn and a half, 'turn a right angle to the left/right', 'turn half a right angle' or 'turn 90°/180°/360°'.
- Draw a compass on the hall floor; make the direction in which the children are originally facing

nominally north. (Alternatively, use a compass to find true north and start the children off facing that way.) Ask the children to predict, before each movement, what direction they will be facing when it is complete.

- Write each of the set of movements on an A4 card. Shuffle the cards and draw them one at a time. This set of movement cards can also be used for further practice by a group working independently.

EXTENSIONS

- A group can do follow-up work with a floor robot, programming it to make a series of turns. This is particularly effective with two floor robots side by side, programmed by different groups: can the robots be made to 'dance' together, following the same sequence?
- Photocopiable page 73 can be used to consolidate work on turning and practise using the four compass directions. The answers are: 1. south, 2. west, 3. east, 4. north, 5. east, 6. north, 7. east, 8. north. The sheet can be used a second time by changing the original starting direction for each set of instructions to east, south or west.

COMPASS MOVES

Whole class
10 minutes, repeated several times over a fortnight

AIM

To consider angles of turn on a compass.

WHAT YOU WILL NEED

A large compass drawn on the board (or on sugar paper, which can be left permanently on display), marked with four points (Y3/P4) or eight points (Y4/P5, more experienced Y3/P4).

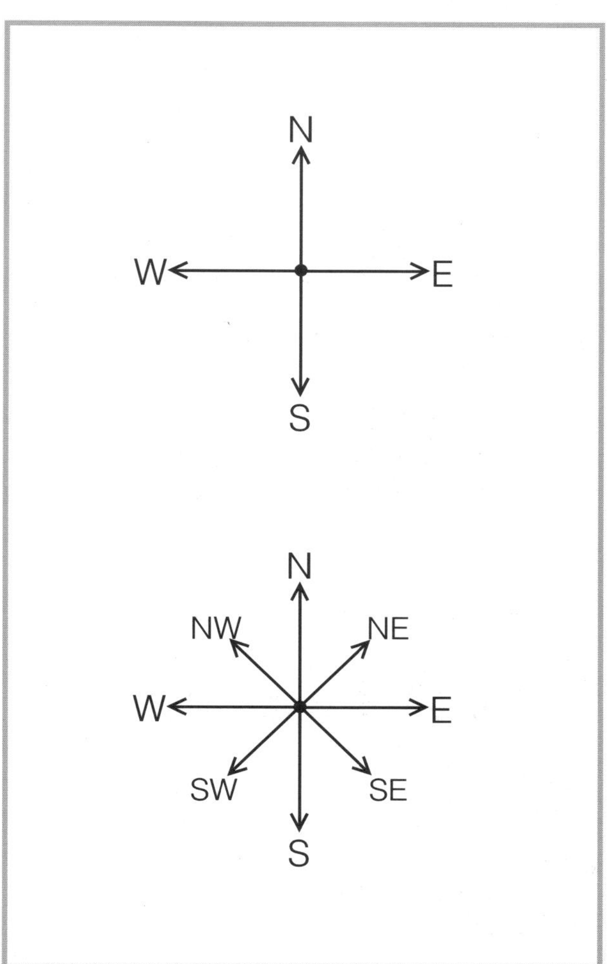

WHAT TO DO

Ask the children to look at the displayed compass drawing and imagine themselves facing north. Give several instructions such as:

- *Imagine turning one right angle [or two, three or four right angles] to the left [or to the right, or clockwise/anti-clockwise]. What direction will you be facing?*

Now give some similar instructions with the children imagining themselves initially facing south, west or east.

Now ask the children to imagine facing in one direction (for example, north) and then turning to face another direction (for example, east). Ask:

- *How many right angles have you turned?*

For each of these exercises, once the children understand what to do, you can nominate a child to give the instruction.

DISCUSSION QUESTIONS

- *How can you work out which direction you will be facing?*
- *How do you know what angle you have turned through?*

ASSESSMENT

Can the children follow the turning sequences? Can they predict the number of turns needed to face a given direction?

VARIATIONS

- *Give instructions of the form 'Turn 90°', 'Turn 180°' and 'Turn 360°'.*
- *Using the eight-point compass, ask the children to turn 'half a right angle' or 'one and a half right angles'. Alternatively, ask them to turn '45°' or '90° and 45°'.*

EXTENSIONS

- Make up a set of cards with the eight (or four) compass points written on, one direction per card. Mark a compass on the floor and place a floor robot facing north. The children can take turns to draw a card and program the robot to turn and face the direction indicated on the card.
- Photocopiable page 74 can be used for follow-up work on angles of turn and compass directions. The answers are: 1. west, 2. west, 3. south-west, 4. east, 5. north, 6. south-east.

CLOCK ANGLES

Whole class and groups
10 minutes, repeated several times over a fortnight

AIMS
To identify angles using the hands on a clock face. To recognize 30° and 60° angles.

WHAT YOU WILL NEED
A large clock face drawn on the board (or on sugar paper, which can be left permanently on display), geared or card clocks (one per group).

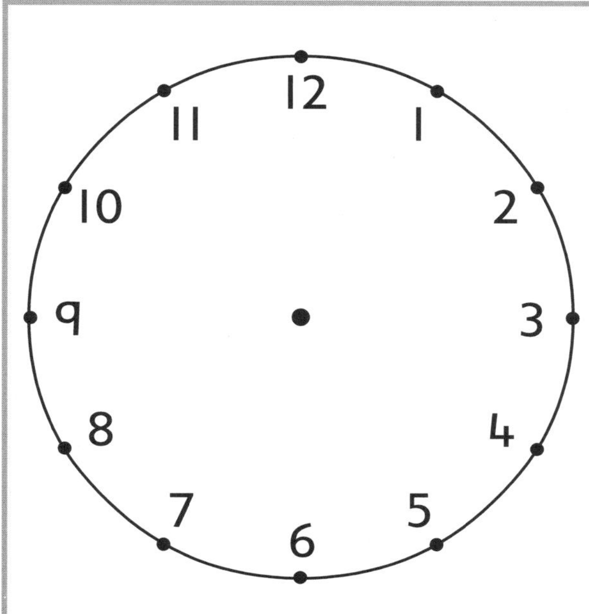

WHAT TO DO
Ask the children to suggest where you might position the hands on the clock face in order to make a right (90°) angle. It is likely that they will suggest vertical and horizontal pairings to begin with (for example, the hands pointing towards 12 and 3, or 6 and 9). Use a geared or card clock to show that turning one hand from 12 to 3 means that it turns by 90°. If no-one realises that other pairings are possible, then demonstrate one (the hands pointing towards 4 and 7) and ask the children to find similar pairings.

Once the children have understood this idea, the clock face can be used to introduce 30° angles: there are three 'hour marks' within a 90° angle. Moving a hand from 4 to 5 is a turn of 30° (since 90 ÷ 3 = 30). Similarly, 60° angles can be introduced: the turn from 4 to 6 must be 2 × 30° = 60°.

Ask the children to find further examples of 30° and 60° angles on the clock face. They can use geared or card clocks to help them if necessary.

DISCUSSION QUESTIONS
- *How can you tell which numbers on the clock face have a right angle between them?*
- *Which numbers have 30°/60° between them?*

ASSESSMENT
Can the children identify right angles on a clock face? Can they identify 30° and 60° angles on a clock face?

EXTENSIONS
- Mark a clock face on the floor and place a floor robot facing the 12 mark. The children can take turns to program the robot to turn and face another clock number (of their choice, or on a card drawn from a pack labelled 1–12).
- Photocopiable page 75 can be used for consolidation work on angles between the hands of a clock.

NAME DATE

ANGLE SIZES

■ Order the angles in each set from the smallest to the largest.

1.

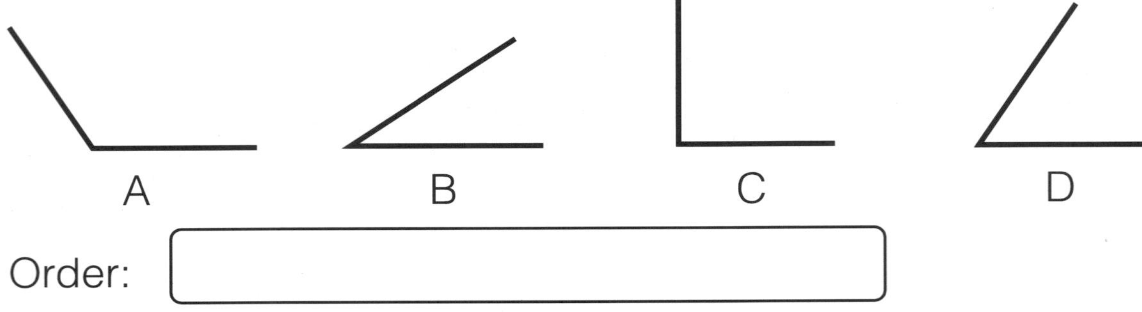

A B C D

Order:

2.

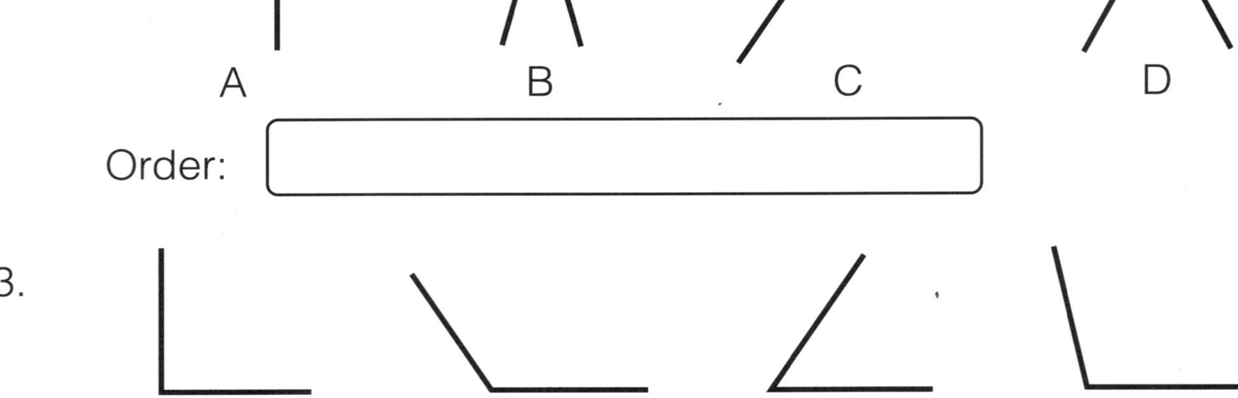

A B C D

Order:

3.

A B C D

Order:

■ Draw one angle smaller and one angle larger than each of these angles:

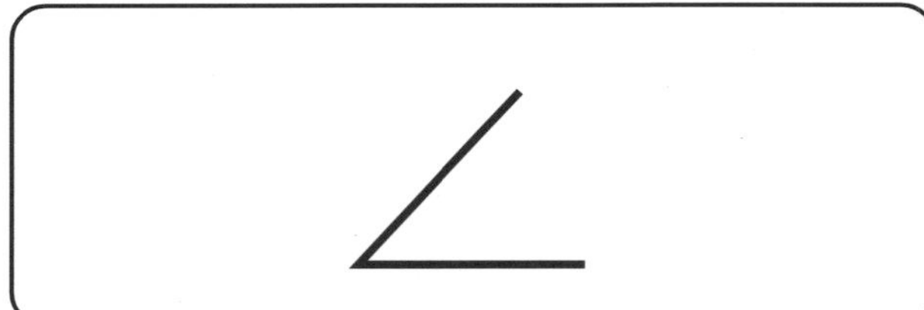

How did you decide the order in each set of angles? Tell your teacher.

SEE 'HUNT THE RIGHT ANGLES', PAGE 64.

NAME DATE

ANGLE COLOURS

- Use colours to mark all of the angles on these shapes:
  - RED – Right angles.
  - BLUE – Angles greater than a right angle.
  - GREEN – Angles less than a right angle.

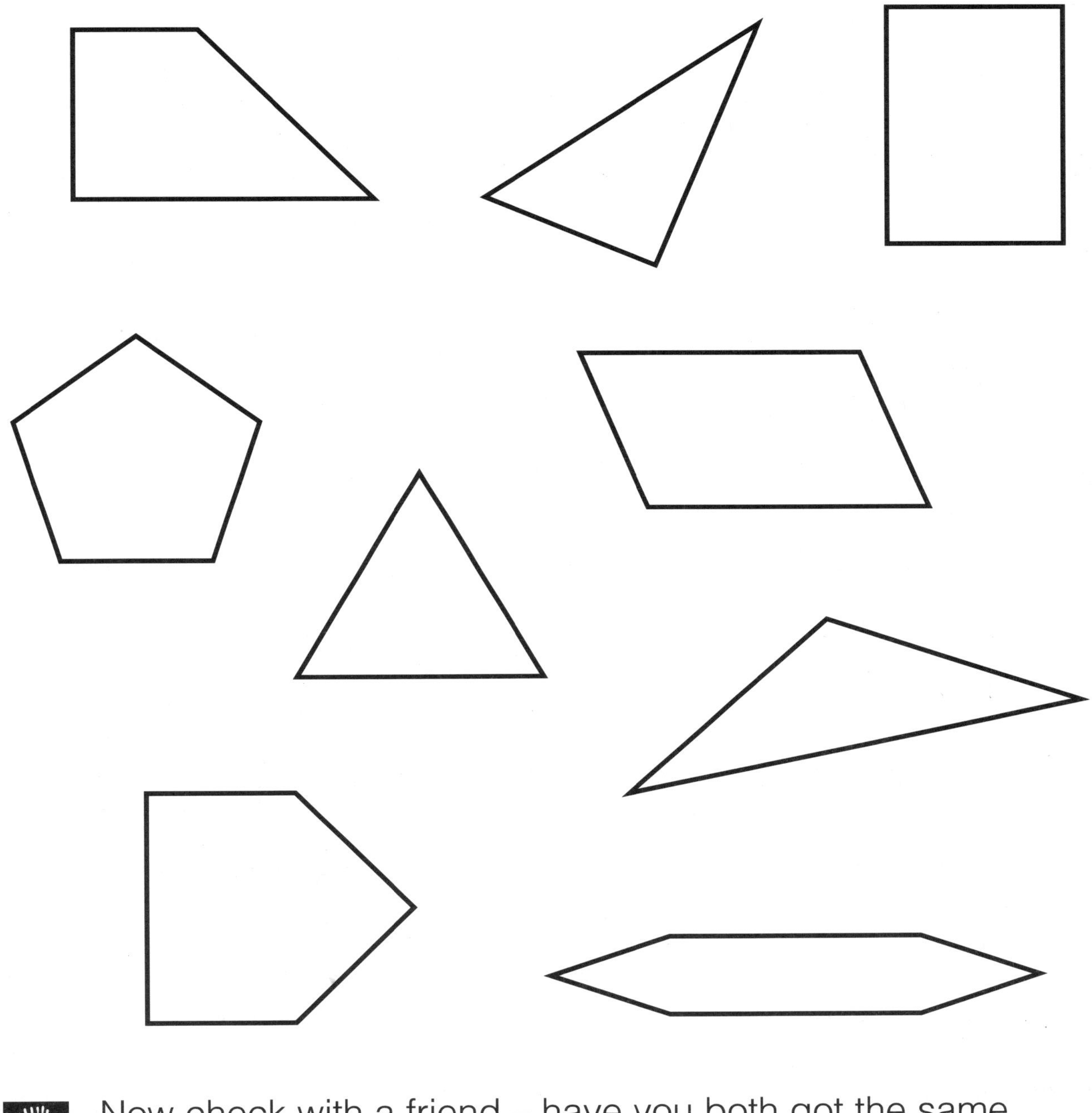

Now check with a friend – have you both got the same number of red, blue and green angles?

SEE 'HUNT THE RIGHT ANGLES', PAGE 64.

ANGLES

NAME DATE

DRAW THE SHAPES

A shape with four right angles.	A shape with no right angles.
A shape with at least one angle greater than 90°.	A shape with at least two angles greater than 90°.
A shape with at least one angle less than 90°.	A shape with at least two angles less than 90°.
A shape with one angle greater than 90° and one angle less than 90°.	A shape with three different types of angle.

Swap with a friend to check each other's shapes.

SEE 'HUNT THE RIGHT ANGLES', PAGE 64.

NAME DATE

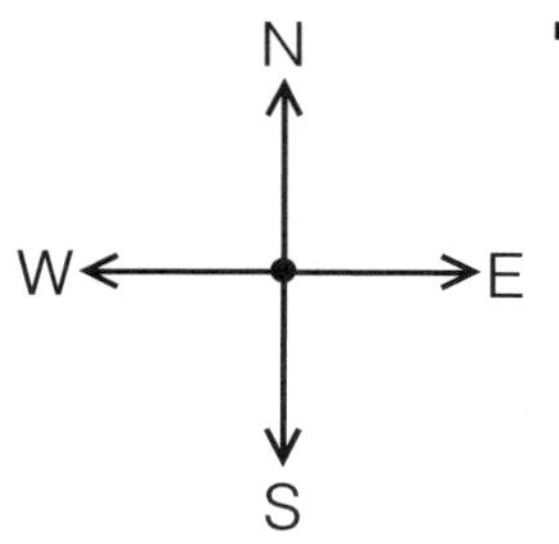

TURN AND TURN AGAIN

■ Follow these instructions. Which direction will you be facing after each one? The first answer has been found for you.

1. Face north. Turn a half-turn to the right. Now facing? south
2. Face north. Turn a quarter-turn anti-clockwise. Now facing?
3. Face north. Turn a half-turn right, then a quarter-turn left. Now facing?
4. Face north. Turn a quarter-turn clockwise, then a quarter-turn anti-clockwise. Now facing?
5. Face north. Turn half a turn to the left, a quarter-turn to the right, then half a turn to the left. Now facing?
6. Face north. Turn a quarter-turn right, a three-quarters turn left, then half a turn right. Now facing?
7. Face north. Turn half a turn clockwise, a quarter-turn anti-clockwise, then a whole turn clockwise. Now facing?
8. Face north. Turn a quarter-turn anti-clockwise, a half-turn clockwise, then a quarter-turn anti-clockwise. Now facing?

Check your answers with a friend. Which were easier to work out? Which were harder?

SEE 'TURN AROUND', PAGE 66.

NAME DATE

COMPASS ANGLES

■ For each of these problems, mark the turn on the compass and write down which direction you are facing after the turn.

1\.

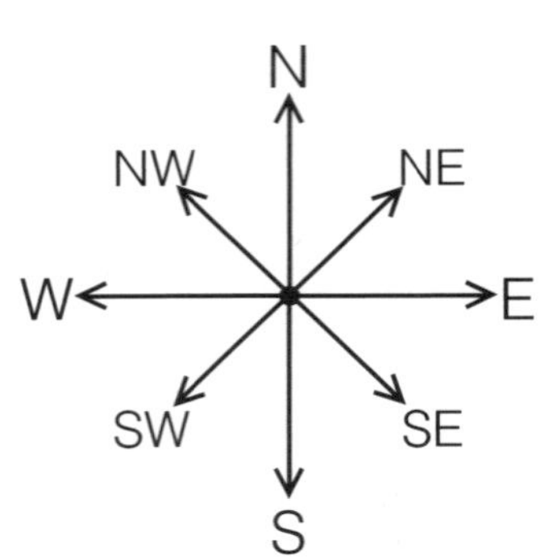

Face north, turn a right angle to the left.

Now facing?

4\.

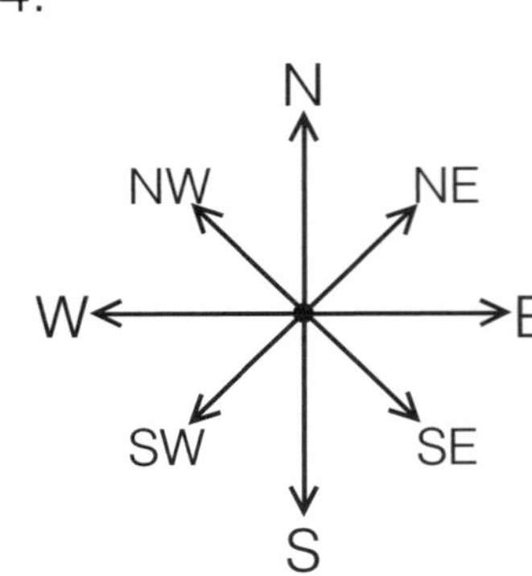

Face south, turn 3 right angles clockwise.

Now facing?

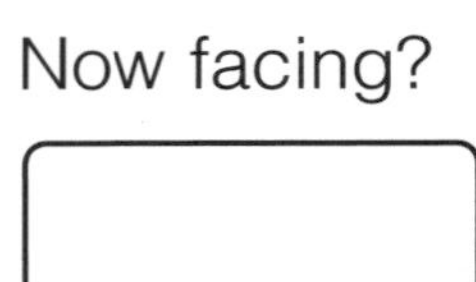

2\.

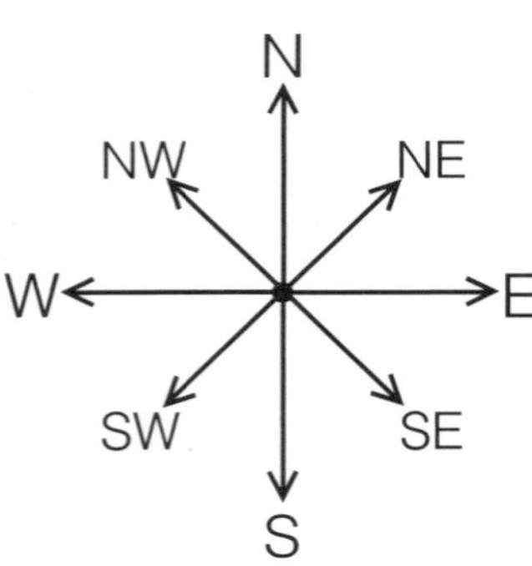

Face east, turn 2 right angles to the right.

Now facing?

5\.

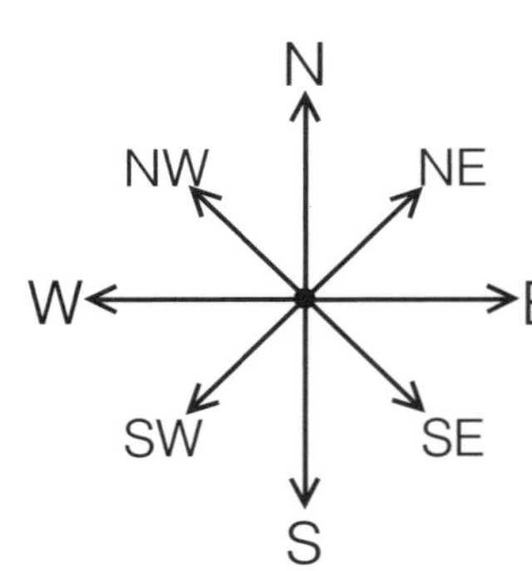

Face west, turn 3 right angles anti-clockwise.

Now facing?

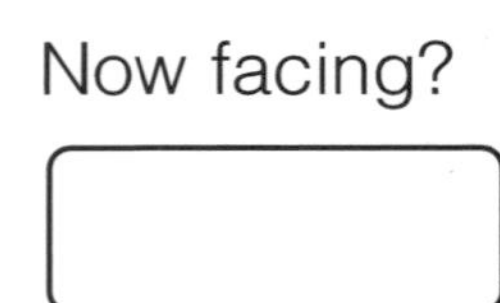

3\.

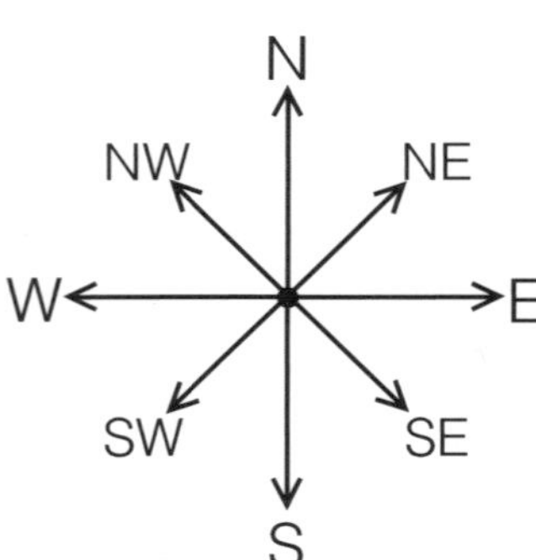

Face south-east, turn a right angle to the right.

Now facing?

6\.

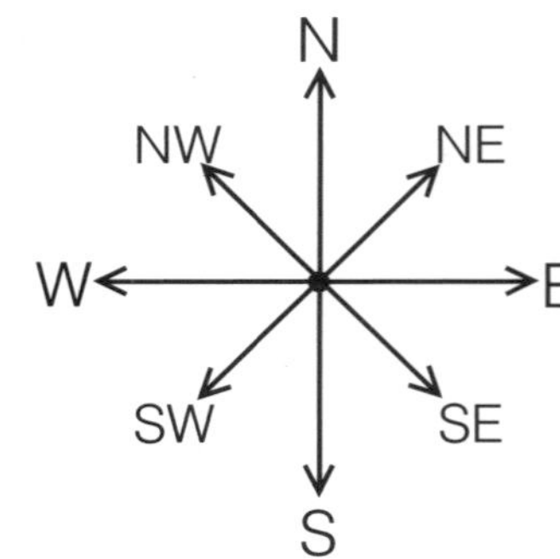

Face north-west, turn 2 right angles to the right.

Now facing?

On the back of the sheet, draw four compasses and make up a problem like these for each one. Swap them with a friend to try.

SEE 'COMPASS MOVES', PAGE 67 (ALSO SEE 'MOVING ARMS', PAGE 65).

NAME DATE

CLOCK IT IN

■ Mark hands to make a right angle on each clock:

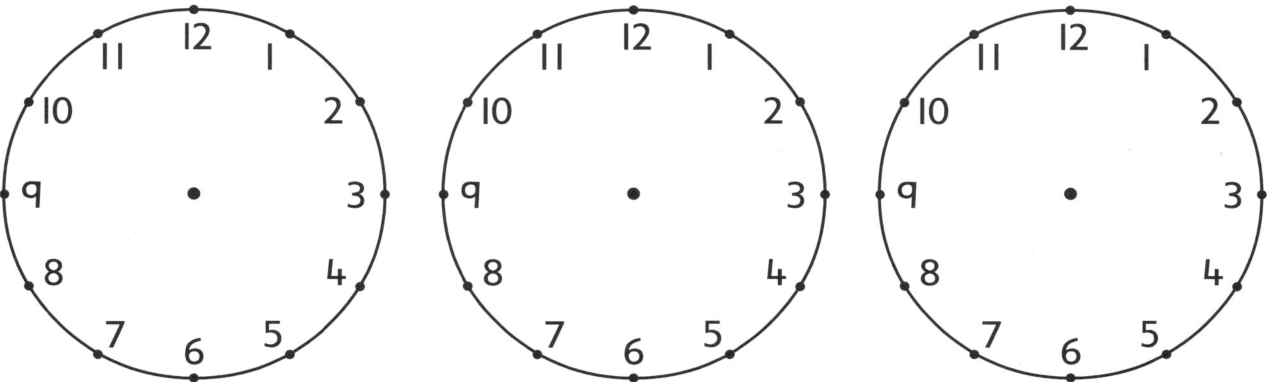

■ Mark hands to make an angle less than a right angle on each clock:

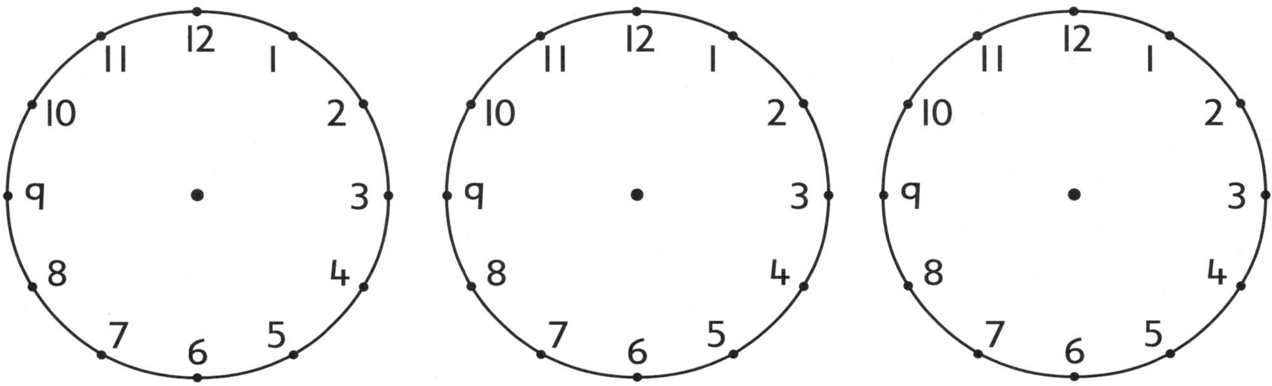

■ Mark hands to make an angle greater than a right angle on each clock:

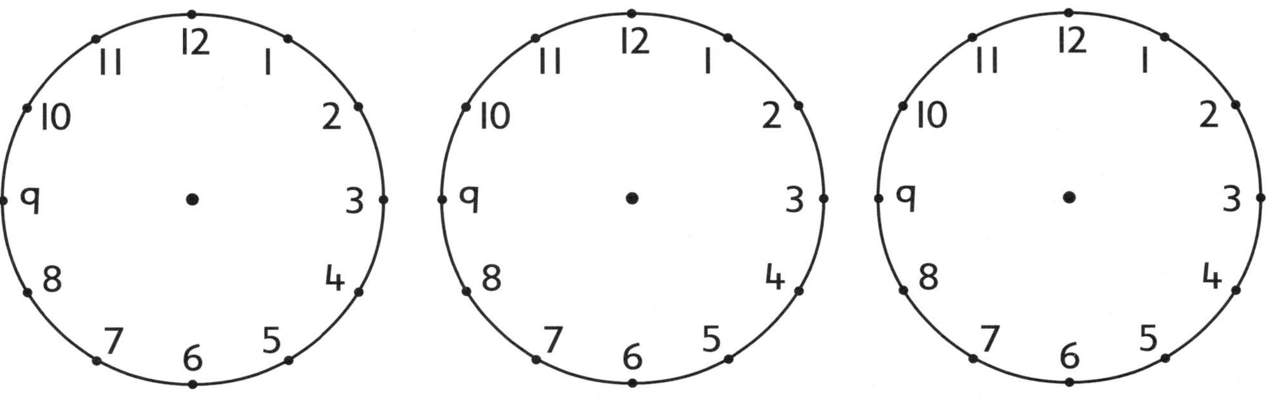

On the back of this sheet write some instructions for a friend, explaining how to solve these problems.

SEE 'CLOCK ANGLES', PAGE 69 (ALSO SEE 'MOVING ARMS', PAGE 65).

LENGTH & AREA

Length measures distance.

Length vocabulary

long short tall
high low
wide narrow
deep shallow
thick thin

Comparing lengths

- Comparing two things: use **longer** and **shorter**.
- Comparing more than two things: use **longest** and **shortest**.

Length is measured in **metres (m)**, **centimetres (cm)** and **kilometres (km)**.
Remember:

- **100cm = 1m**
- **1000m = 1km**

Area measures surface.

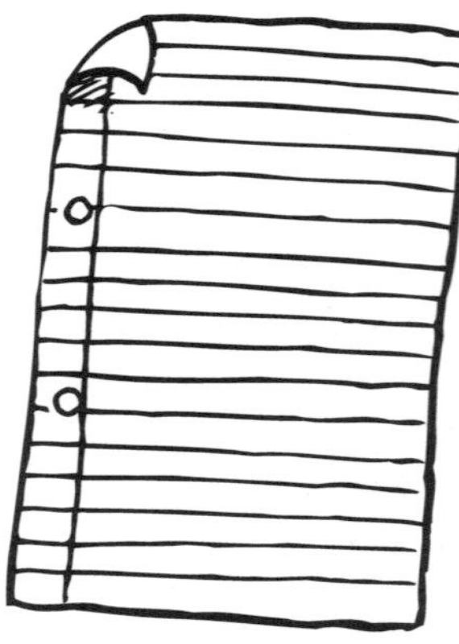

Area vocabulary

surface
covers

Measuring area

Area is measured in **square centimetres**, which can be written as **cm²**.

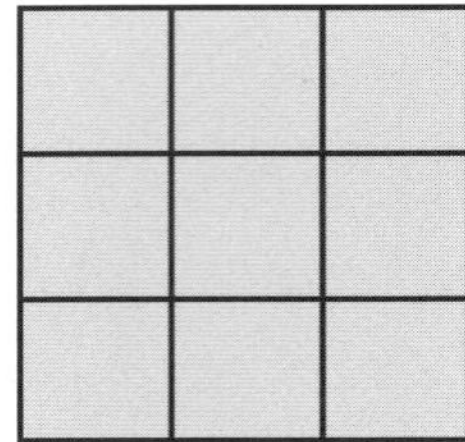

Area = $9cm^2$

MASS

Mass measures the amount of something.

Mass vocabulary

big small
heavy light
balance scales

Units of mass

Mass is measured in **grams (g)** and **kilograms (kg)**.
Remember:
1000g = 1kg

CAPACITY

Capacity measures the amount of space something can contain.

An amount of space is called a **volume**. So the **capacity** of a cup is the same thing as the **volume** of water that it can hold.

Capacity vocabulary

full	half full	empty
contains	holds	

Units of capacity

Capacity is measured in **litres (l)** and **millilitres (ml)**.
Remember:
1000ml = 1l

TIME

Time measures the length of an event.

Time vocabulary

days	months	seasons
week	weekend	
fortnight	month	
hour	minute	second
year	leap year	
decade	century	millennium
today	tomorrow	yesterday
timetable	analogue clock	digital clock

analogue *digital*

Measuring time

Time has many different units.
Remember:

- **1 minute = 60 seconds**
- **60 minutes = 1 hour**
- **24 hours = 1 day**
- **7 days = 1 week**
- **1 year = 52 weeks**
- **100 years = 1 century**
- **1000 years = 1 millennium**

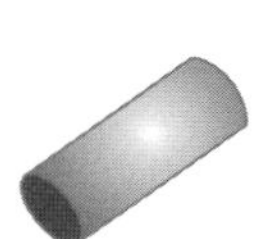

KEY IDEAS

- Length is a measure of distance.
- Not all lengths are simple straight-line measures.
- The metre is the standard unit of length. Centimetres (for smaller lengths) and kilometres (for greater lengths) are commonly used.
- The distance all around an object or shape is called its perimeter.
- Area is a measure of the amount of surface covered.

Length is the most tangible of all the measures that children learn about in primary school. It is usually possible to tell just by looking that one object is longer than another. As they get older, children should move beyond this simple comparison; by Year 3/Primary 4, they should have encountered the standard units (metres and centimetres). However, you should not assume that all the children are sure about this: early activities in this section aim to consolidate the vocabulary of length, as well as a sense of what is being measured. It is important that children know what 1cm and 1m look like, instead of simply reciting '100cm = 1 metre'. At this stage, it is not necessary to use imperial units (inches, feet, yards and miles); looking at metric and imperial units together is likely to cause confusion. However, you should be aware that children may encounter these units outside school.

Children need to explore a range of regular non-standard units as well as standard ones. Estimating with each helps them to build up a sense of distance. However, children have difficulty with estimating and often prefer to invent their 'estimates' retrospectively. This probably derives from the perception that maths always has to produce 'right answers'! The 'range' method introduced here (also see the 'Mass and capacity' section) is an attempt to avoid this difficulty.

Perimeter and area are linked to length. Perimeter is the distance all round a shape. The area of a shape is the amount of 2-D surface it covers. Understanding area is linked to spatial perception, especially ideas about tessellation. At this stage, it is important to focus on consolidating the children's understanding of the general concept of area. To begin with, areas can be found by counting squares. More formal work is introduced at the end of this section (for example, leading to the idea that the area of a triangle is the product of its length and width).

BY THE END OF Y3/P4, MOST CHILDREN SHOULD BE ABLE TO:

- read and begin to write the vocabulary related to length
- measure and compare using standard units
- use a ruler to draw and measure lines to the nearest half centimetre
- know the relationship between kilometres and metres, and between metres and centimetres
- begin to use decimal notation (for example, recognize 3.05m as 3 metres and 5 centimetres)
- suggest suitable units and measuring equipment to estimate or measure lengths in cm, m or km, and record estimates and measurements.

BY THE END OF Y4/P5, MOST CHILDREN SHOULD BE ABLE TO:

- use, read and write standard metric units, including their abbreviations (mm, cm, m, km)
- use the relationships between units
- tell you the equivalents of one half, one quarter, three quarters and one tenth of 1km and 1m in m and cm
- suggest suitable units (including miles) and measuring equipment to estimate or measure length, and record estimates and measurements to a suitable degree of accuracy
- measure and start to calculate the perimeter and area of rectangles and other simple shapes
- understand that area is conserved when the pieces of a shape are rearranged.

SOME COMMON MISCONCEPTIONS AND STRATEGIES FOR CORRECTING THEM

HEIGHT, LENGTH, WIDTH, DEPTH OR THICKNESS?

These words all represent measures of linear distance. Sometimes we change the word when we change orientation – for example, if you look at a cuboid from different directions, the 'length' will become the 'depth'. The word 'depth' is also difficult because it can refer both to 'downwards height' (as in a pool) and to horizontal distance 'inwards' (as on a shelf).

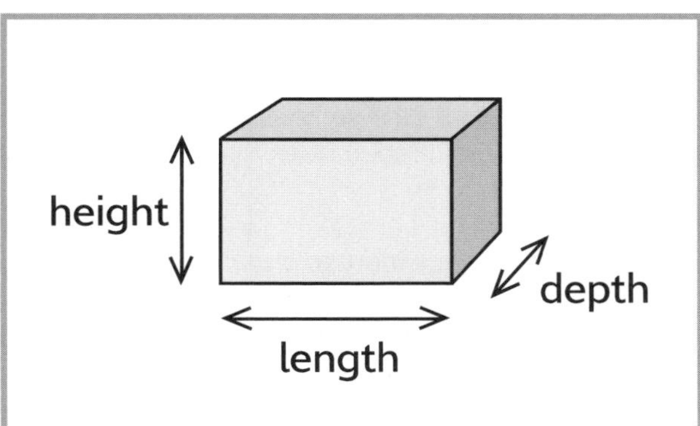

Confusion about the meanings of these terms can be overcome by working with a range of 3-D objects and discussing what is being measured each time.

COMPARING

The use of comparative terms (long, longer, longest) is linguistically difficult for some children. It may also lead to confusion, as the longer of two objects may also be the shorter of a different pair.

Use a range of real-life objects, such as books and pencils, to reinforce this point.

USING A RULER

Children need to be reminded to line up one end of an object with '0cm' on their ruler. On many rulers, '0cm' is a little way in from the edge of the ruler. Many common rulers have 'inches' as well as 'centimetres' marked on them, and some come marked in millimetres rather than centimetres. Choose your class set of rulers with care!

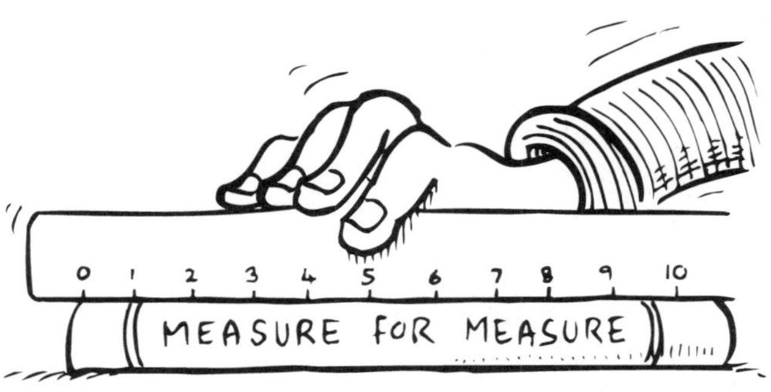

AREA AND PERIMETER

Confusion between area and perimeter often occurs when children start using formulae to calculate them before they have a secure understanding of the concepts. Use practical examples to emphasize that area relates to the whole surface, whereas perimeter relates only to the edge.

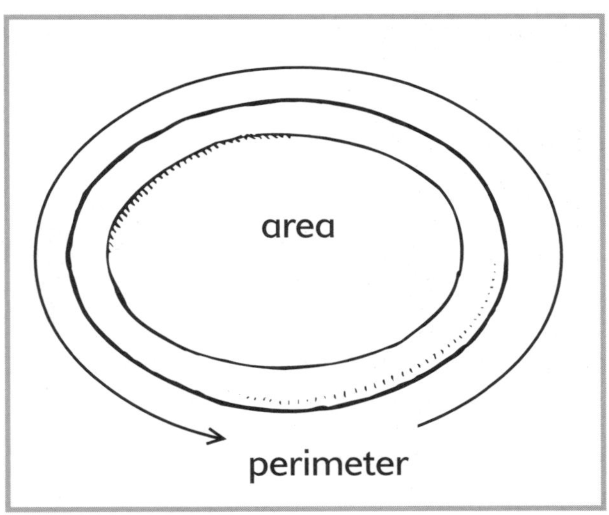

SHOW ME THE LENGTH

Whole class
20 minutes

AIM
To develop a 'feel' for different lengths.

WHAT YOU WILL NEED
A 30cm ruler, a metre stick (with 50cm prominently marked).

WHAT TO DO
Hold up a 30cm ruler. Ask the children to look at it. Say that the ruler is 30cm long. Now ask them to close their eyes and hold up their hands (with the palms facing) to show you how long the ruler is – without peeking! Now ask them to open their eyes, without moving their hands. Is everyone's 30cm the same?

Now ask for three or four volunteers (choose children whose responses were quite varied). They should stand facing the class with their eyes closed. Again, ask them to hold out their hands with the palms facing to show the length of the ruler. Ask the rest of the class to suggest whose hands' distance is closest to 30cm. Give one child a ruler to check. Check the others too, then ask the class to direct the volunteers (one at a time) to move their hands closer or further apart until they are showing 30cm.

Together or in small groups, the children can now

try the same activity for distances of 10cm or 20cm. The activity can be repeated another time, using a metre stick and asking the children to show a metre or half metre distance with their hands.

DISCUSSION QUESTIONS
- *How can you tell how far apart your hands are?*
- *Who is underestimating the distances? Who is overestimating?*
- *Does anyone know a good way of checking?*

ASSESSMENT
Do the children demonstrate or develop a good sense of centimetre and metre lengths?

VARIATION
The children could try the same activity with their eyes open. What difference does this make?

EXTENSIONS
- As the children gain more experience, target more difficult lengths such as 7cm, 15cm or 25cm.
- Ask two children to stand a given number of metres apart.
- Photocopiable page 90 can be used as a complement to this activity: it requires the children to distinguish between the relative sizes of centimetres, metres and kilometres by deciding whether some stated lengths of objects are sensible. The answers are: 2, 3, 4 and 8 are right; 1, 5, 6 and 7 are wrong.

HOW LONG? (1)

Groups of three or four
50 minutes

AIMS
To estimate using non-standard units, using the concept of 'range'. To distinguish between uniform and non-uniform measures.

WHAT YOU WILL NEED
A collection of things to measure (table length, board width, a piece of sugar paper, a poster tube and so on); a collection of things to measure with (straws, playing cards, dominoes, pencils, books and so on); paper, pencils.

WHAT TO DO
Take a straw from a packet, hold it up and ask the children to estimate how many straws will fit across the table. Show them how to estimate using the 'range' method: estimating a minimum and maximum number of straws. When the class have agreed a suitable range, ask one pair to carry out the measurement. As the table is unlikely to be an exact number of straws across, show the children how to

round up or down (depending on the size of the 'bit left over') to find the nearest whole number of straws.

Now ask the children to estimate the number of pencils that will fit across the table. Ask a couple of children to find their pencils (alternatively, have a pair of pencils ready: one nearly new, one well-used and short). The point to draw out here is that the answer with the pencils will depend on whose pencil is used: pencils are an example of **non-uniform** items, whereas the straws used initially are of **uniform** length.

Ask the children to suggest further examples of uniform and non-uniform items to measure with. A uniform measure is one that everyone will get the same answer with; a non-uniform item is one that will produce different answers. Draw up a list on the board or flip chart, adding your own examples if necessary. Dominoes and playing cards (from the same set) and class exercise books are good examples of uniform measures. Good examples of non-uniform measures are any body measure, such as the handspan or stride.

Draw the table shown below on the board or flip chart. Working in groups of three or four, the children should copy this table and spend time estimating and measuring at least five different things.

Bring the class back together to review their findings. Remind them of the traditional story of the carpenter's apprentice, who made a tiny bed for the queen because he measured 'six feet' with his own small feet.

DISCUSSION QUESTIONS

- *Who can explain why this object will give us the same answer every time?*
- *Who can explain why this object will NOT give us the same answer every time?*
- *What is the most/least anyone thinks the answer might be? Can we narrow the range a little?*
- *What objects do you like measuring with? Why?*

Object	Measured with	Estimate: Minimum	Estimate: Maximum	Actual number
Table top	Straws			
Length of room	Strides			

ASSESSMENT

Do the children appreciate the difference between uniform and non-uniform measures of length? Can they develop sensible estimates using the 'range' method? Can they measure various objects using a variety of uniform and non-uniform measures of length?

VARIATION

This activity could be divided into two separate sessions: estimating with uniform units and non-uniform units on different occasions.

EXTENSIONS

- The **Group problem-solving** activity 'How long? (2)' (page 87) follows on from this activity.
- 'What's the mass?' (page 101) explores the use of similar concepts in estimating mass. 'Cover up' (page 89) explores the estimation of area using a variety of non-standard measures.

HALF THE LENGTH

Whole class, then individuals
50 minutes

AIMS

To practise measuring accurately. To make a scale drawing.

WHAT YOU WILL NEED

A range of objects for drawing (such as books, pencil cases, small toys); rulers, paper, pencils.

WHAT TO DO

Spend five minutes on a quick revision of halving numbers. Check that the children know that halving an odd number will result in 'something and a half' – for example, half of 13 is 6½.

Give each child an object and a ruler. Ask the children to measure the length (or height) of their object. Remind them about lining up the zero mark on the ruler with the end of the object. Now ask them to halve the length and to write down both the original and the half length. Check that they have done this. Repeat this process for the width. Now ask them to draw a picture of their object with the length and width halved. Stress the need for care and accuracy. Finally, they should swap drawings with a partner and work out the original dimensions of each object.

DISCUSSION QUESTIONS

- *How can we measure accurately with a ruler?*
- *How can you be sure this is half the length of that?*

ASSESSMENT

Can the children measure accurately? Can they create accurate scale drawings, halving the width as well as the length?

EXTENSIONS

- The children can use larger objects and draw pictures one third or one quarter the actual dimensions.
- They can use smaller objects and draw pictures double or treble the actual dimensions.
- They can pair up, then measure and draw each other to a scale of one fifth or one tenth the actual dimensions.
- They can use the writing frame on resource page 128 to report on this activity.

WALKING THE EDGE

Whole class
10 minutes, repeated several times

AIM

To develop a 'feel' for the perimeter of a shape.

WHAT YOU WILL NEED

A collection of large 2-D shapes: circle, triangle, square, oblong, hexagon and so on.

WHAT TO DO

Ask a volunteer to walk from corner to corner of the classroom (if this is tricky because of furniture arrangements, use the school hall). Introduce the term **perimeter** in this context as *the journey around the edges of the classroom.*

Hold up a square shape. Ask the children to close their eyes and imagine they have shrunk down in size, so that they can stand in a corner of this square. Ask them to imagine walking around the edges of the square until they are back where they started. Now ask a child to describe the journey. Ask another child to describe it as well – not everyone will see it in the same way. Encourage them to use the language of position, direction and angle.

This activity can be repeated for other shapes, and used as a starter activity for any of the subsequent sessions on the topic of perimeter.

DISCUSSION QUESTIONS

- *How can you tell when you are back where you started?*
- *Which shapes are interesting to walk around? Why?*

ASSESSMENT

Do the children understand and use the word 'perimeter' to refer to the distance around a shape? Do they use appropriate vocabulary to describe journeys around shapes?

EXTENSIONS

- The children can describe their journeys around shapes in writing.
- They can use less regular shapes, such as the tetrominoes (see page 40).
- Describe a journey around the edges of a shape. Can the children work out which shape you are walking around?

THE LARGEST PIECE

Whole class, then pairs
20 minutes

AIM

To understand the conservation of area.

WHAT YOU WILL NEED

Paper squares (around 8cm × 8cm), an OHP and/or display board with pins or Blu-Tack.

WHAT TO DO

Give each child a paper square. Tell them that the size of the paper (how much of the desk it covers) is its **area**, and they will be investigating this. Ask the children to fold their square of paper in half, then in half again. Do not say *how* they should do this. There are three basic ways (see illustration):

- fold vertically, then horizontally, making a smaller square
- fold vertically, then again vertically, making a thin rectangle
- fold diagonally, then again diagonally, making a small triangle.

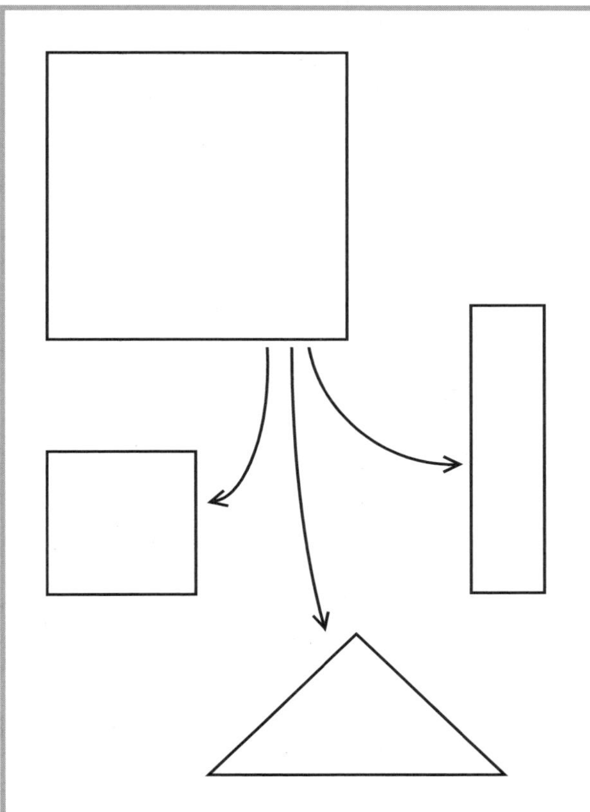

Hopefully, each of these will be produced by at least one child. (To be on the safe side, you might want to prepare a set of the three possible quarters.) Ask the children to examine their quarter squares. *Is everyone's quarter the same?* Now pin up one of each (or place them on an OHT), and ask: *Which is the largest piece?*

After some discussion, the children should pair up with three new pieces of paper each. They should make each of the quarters, this time cutting along the folds. Challenge them to find a way to prove that all three types of quarter have the same area. (The easiest way to do this is to cut the rectangle and the triangle in half again, and reassemble the pieces to make the small square.)

DISCUSSION QUESTIONS

- *If the pieces of paper were pieces of cake, which quarter would you rather have? Why?*
- *Why do the pieces not look as if they have the same area?*
- *Who can explain why all the pieces* do *have the same area?*

ASSESSMENT

Do the children realize why all the quarters have the same area? How articulately can they demonstrate or explain this result?

EXTENSIONS

- The children can fold a paper square into eighths in various ways, then show that they are all equal in area.
- The 'Cut and paste' activity (see the '2-D and 3-D shapes' section, page 16) also demonstrates how shapes that look different can have the same area.
- Work with tangrams (see pages 22 and 53) can also be used to discuss the conservation of area: any figures made with all of the tangram pieces will have the same area, despite some 'looking bigger' because the pieces are more spread out.
- Photocopiable page 93 reinforces the idea that different shapes can have the same area.

MEASURE YOUR HAND

Whole class, then individuals
50 minutes

AIMS
To understand that areas cannot be compared by a linear measure. To find area by counting squares. To become aware of 'square centimetres' as a measure of area.

WHAT YOU WILL NEED
1cm squared paper, pencils; collections of various objects (such as leaves, lids, plastic shapes).

WHAT TO DO
Ask the children to pair up and compare their left hands (with the fingers held together). *Can you decide whose hand is larger?* Ask the pairs to put their left hands together. It is easy to tell which hand is longer or wider – but explain that this is not the same as **larger**.

Show the children some 1cm squared paper. Ask them to imagine drawing around their left hand on the paper and counting the number of squares. *How many squares do you think your hand will cover?* Explain that this is a good way to compare the size of two hands, since it takes account of both the length and the width.

Introduce the children to the method of finding area by counting squares. Part squares should be counted if they are more than a half, but not counted if they are less than a half. The children should now draw around their hands on squared paper (they might find it easier to work in pairs, drawing around each other's hands), then count the squares to find the area. Encourage the use of 'square centimetres' (sq cm or cm^2) as units of area.

When the children have measured and compared the area of their hands, they can compare the area of their footprints in a similar way.

DISCUSSION QUESTIONS
- *How can you compare the size of your hands? What is a fair method?*
- *How can you be sure that this shape is larger than that shape?*

ASSESSMENT
Can the children successfully compare their hand areas?

EXTENSIONS
- The children can use squared paper to compare the area covered by their closed hand (fist) with the area covered by their hand with all the fingers stretched wide.
- They can refine the square counting method by counting half units of area for any square that looks about half covered.
- Give the children a range of objects (such as a leaf, a lid, a plastic shape and so on) and ask them to order these according to area. They should discuss this and agree on an order before drawing round each object and finding the area (by counting squares).
- Ask the children to draw an outline hand or foot that has a given area, such as $20cm^2$ or $30cm^2$.
- Photocopiable page 94 can be used for individual work to consolidate measuring area by counting squares.

FIVE SQUARES

Whole class, then individuals
50 minutes

AIM
To understand the conservation of area.

WHAT YOU WILL NEED
1cm squared paper, pencils, an OHP (optional).

WHAT TO DO
This activity is best explained by demonstration, using a piece of 1cm squared paper on an OHP (ideally) or a grid of squares drawn on the board or flip chart. Show the children some different arrangements of five squares (see figure below). The only rule is that the squares must be touching, either side to side or corner to corner – but they must not overlap.

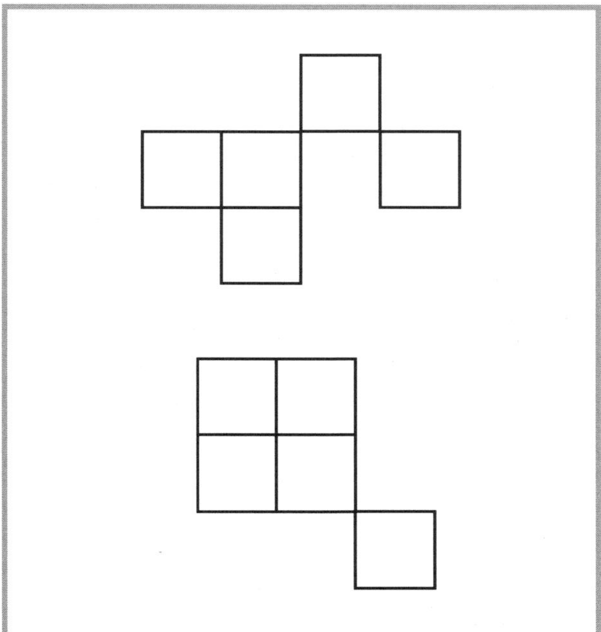

Now hand out 1cm squared paper and ask the children to create ten more 'five-square' designs. Explain that these will all have the same area.

During the plenary session, ask children to describe their favourite design to you while you try to recreate it. A collection of five-square designs will make a good classroom display.

DISCUSSION QUESTIONS
- *Can you explain why these two designs have the same area?*

ASSESSMENT
Can the children create a range of designs using five squares? Can they explain why these designs all have the same area?

VARIATION
- The children can make designs using a smaller or greater number of squares.

EXTENSIONS
- The children can also consider the perimeters of their shapes. This will help them to see that shapes with the same area can have different perimeters. More able children can explore this more formally by completing photocopiable page 95 (they will need 1cm squared paper for this).
- The children can use geoboards to create different shapes with the same area. Resource page 124 can be used to create a variety of shapes with an area of 2, 2½ or 3 squares.
- Allow halving of squares. This creates many further possibilities, such as:

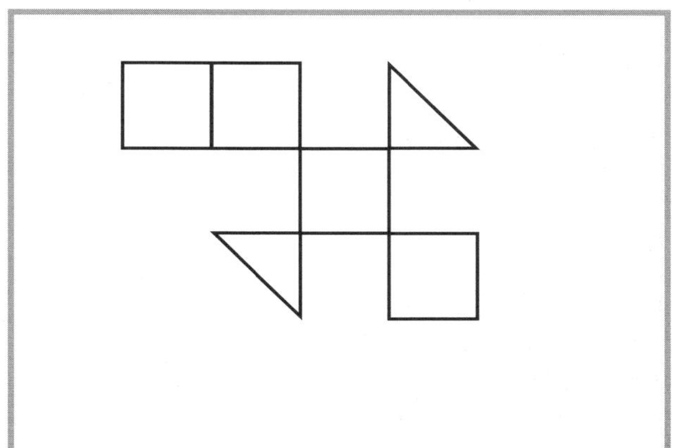

LENGTH & AREA

A TALL TALE

Whole class, then groups
40 minutes

AIMS
To develop vocabulary for comparing lengths. To understand the idea of using a baseline to measure from.

WHAT YOU WILL NEED
Sets of three objects (one set per group), such as: three pencils of different lengths, three books of different thicknesses, three boxes of different widths. A list of vocabulary for display, including: **tall, short, taller, tallest; long, longer, longest; wide, narrow, wider, widest; thick, thin, thicker, thickest**.

WHAT TO DO
Discuss with the children how to compare the height, length, width or thickness of two objects. Explain that the key point is to have a common starting point or baseline: without that, the comparison is not valid. You could recreate the scene in the cartoon below to underline the point. Use three children of different heights to demonstrate 'tall', 'taller', 'tallest'.

Draw the children's attention to the vocabulary list. Ask them to motion with their hands to show the difference between tall, short, thin, thick, long, wide, narrow. Point out that they are not all showing the same length with their hands. People's judgements of length are relative, and this is why we need to have standard units of measurement.

Give each group a set of three objects. Ask them to find a way to order the set of objects according to one kind of linear measurement. For objects such as cardboard boxes, the order may depend on whether the length, width or height is used to make the comparison. You may prefer to give such objects to the more confident children, and to give more straightforward objects (such as three pencils of different lengths) to other groups.

Give the children about 15 minutes to work with the objects. They should draw a labelled picture to show what they have found out, selecting the appropriate mathematical vocabulary from the displayed list.

In the plenary session, ask the groups to give feedback to the whole class.

DISCUSSION QUESTIONS
- *How can you tell which object is the longest (widest, tallest, shortest...)?*
- *What can you say about this object compared to that one?*

ASSESSMENT
Do the children understand how to make the comparisons? Do they use the language of comparison in appropriate ways?

EXTENSIONS
- Provide sets of more than three objects for the children to order.
- Ask the children to find objects that are shorter and longer than the ones they have, as well as ones in between.

HOW LONG? (2)

Whole class, then groups of 3 or 4
50 minutes

AIM
To estimate and measure using standard units of length (metres and centimetres).

WHAT YOU WILL NEED
A collection of things to measure (table length, board width, a sheet of sugar paper, a poster tube and so on); rulers, metre sticks, trundle wheels; pencil, paper.

WHAT TO DO
This activity follows on from 'How long? (1)' (page 80). Start by discussing with the class why we have developed standard units to measure with, and how we can use rulers, metre sticks and trundle wheels accurately for measuring.

Ask them to consider which things are best measured in metres (eg the length and width of the classroom) and which in centimetres (eg books and pencils); draw up a list of each on the board.

Reinforce the idea that 100 centimetres (cm) is equal to 1 metre (m). A useful way to do this is to ask the children to measure the *back* of a 1 metre stick using their rulers.

The children should work in groups of three or four, as in 'How Long (1)', to estimate the length of a number of objects (using the 'range' method), record the estimates, then carry out the measurements using rulers, metre sticks or trundle wheels as appropriate. For greater lengths, the activity could move out into the school hall or playground.

DISCUSSION QUESTIONS
- *How accurately are you estimating? Were you able to narrow the range?*
- *Were you surprised at any of the answers? [This often happens with distances in metres, or with longer objects measured in centimetres.]*

ASSESSMENT
Can the children make sensible estimates? Can they measure objects accurately using rulers, metre sticks and trundle wheels?

VARIATION
The activity could be divided into two separate sessions: one for estimating and measuring in centimetres, the other for estimating and measuring in metres. The latter could take place in the school hall or playground.

EXTENSION
The children can use the writing frame on resource page 128 to write an account of their practical work.

ALL THE WAY ROUND

Whole class, then groups
50 minutes

AIM
To estimate the distance around a non-linear object using standard units.

WHAT YOU WILL NEED
A collection of objects to measure round (PE hoops, cylinders, beakers, a class globe, balls, fruit and so on) string, paper strips, tape measures, rulers, metre sticks; paper, pencils.

WHAT TO DO
This session is concerned with measuring non-linear lengths. Start by asking the class how to measure the distance *around* various objects – for example: *How long is the piece of plastic used to make a PE hoop? How long is the distance around the class globe or around your wrist?* Use a variety of objects to present different challenges, asking the children to suggest ways of measuring curved lengths. They may suggest using a tape measure; or using string or a paper strip which can be wrapped around an object, then pulled straight and measured with a ruler or metre stick. With objects that have a circular cross-section, children may suggest measuring halfway around and then doubling.

Ask the children to work in groups of three or four to measure a range of objects which have a circular 'distance round'. They should use their own choice of materials. In the plenary session, ask the groups to explain their methods for measuring non-linear lengths and to comment on the accuracy of their results.

DISCUSSION QUESTIONS
- *Which objects were easiest/hardest to measure around?*
- *Which method of measuring is easiest?*

ASSESSMENT
Can the children measure non-linear lengths accurately, using a sensible method?

EXTENSIONS
- Ask the children to estimate each 'distance round' before they measure it. (They do not need to be aware of the relationship beween circumference and diameter.)
- The children can use the writing frame on resource page 128 to write an account of their practical work.
- Photocopiable page 91 can be used for follow-up work. The children should realize that they need to use string to measure the lines.

MEASURE THE EDGE

Pairs
40 minutes

AIMS
To understand perimeter as the distance around a shape. To measure the perimeters of a variety of shapes.

WHAT YOU WILL NEED
Plastic shapes (various sizes of circle, triangle, square, oblong and so on) arranged in sets of three or four per pair of children, plus several extra ones; rulers, string, paper, pencils. Each set should contain different shapes and different sizes of the same shape.

WHAT TO DO
Remind the children of the idea of perimeter (see 'Walking the edge', page 82). If necessary, use a child walking around the edges of the classroom or hall to demonstrate this. Now hold up two different shapes that are similar in size. Ask the children how they could tell which shape has the longer perimeter. Hopefully someone will suggest measuring the edges of each shape. Choose a couple of children to do this.

Give each pair a set of shapes. Ask them to examine the shapes and discuss (without formally measuring) which has the longest perimeter, which has the next longest, and so on. They should record their predictions, then measure around each shape using a ruler (or string, in the case of circular shapes). They should then swap shapes with another pair and repeat to confirm each pair's answers.

NB If children realize that perimeter can be calculated (for example, the perimeter of an equilateral triangle is three times the length of one side), then suggest that they measure anyway to check. At this stage, avoid teaching formulae for perimeter, since the main purpose of this activity is to help children develop a 'feel' for perimeter.

DISCUSSION QUESTIONS

- *Why do you think that that shape has the longest/ shortest perimeter?*
- *Does the longest shape have the longest perimeter?*
- *How can you measure the perimeter of the square [circle, triangle, oblong and so on]?*
- *Which shapes are easiest to find the perimeter of? Why?*
- *Can anyone find a shape with a perimeter longer than the perimeter of the square [circle, triangle, oblong and so on]?*

ASSESSMENT

Can the children measure the perimeters of a range of different shapes?

EXTENSIONS

- The children can use a range of irregular shapes.
- They can use the writing frame on resource page 128 for individual reflection on the activity, focusing on the strategies they used for measuring perimeter and anything they have discovered about the shapes.
- Photocopiable page 92 provides a follow-up activity on predicting the relative perimeters of different shapes, then measuring to confirm. Photocopiable page 95 combines measurement of perimeter with measurement of area (see 'Five squares', page 85).

COVER UP

Whole class, then groups
50 minutes

AIM

To understand area in terms of covering surfaces.

WHAT YOU WILL NEED

A3 and A2 sized paper, different-sized sheets of newspaper, collections of various items (such as leaves, paint pots, lids, plastic shapes, cubes and tins).

WHAT TO DO

Explain to the children that you want them to try covering sheets of paper using different objects. Show them a large sheet of paper and ask them to suggest objects with which to cover the whole surface. Remind them of the 'range' method for estimating (see 'How long? (1)' on page 80). Give each group a large sheet of paper, and set them the task of estimating and checking for at least four different objects. They should record their results in table form, perhaps adapting the table used in 'How long? (1)' (page 80).

When all the groups have done this, bring the class together to discuss their findings (see questions below).

DISCUSSION QUESTIONS

- *What are good shapes for measuring area? Why?*
- *What happens when you measure a surface with leaves [or lids, plastic circles, cubes...]?*

ASSESSMENT

Do the children make sensible estimates? Can they explain why some objects are better for covering surfaces than others? Do they organize the objects to cover as much of the paper as possible?

EXTENSIONS

- Include non-rectangular surfaces (for example, large circles) to be covered.
- Work on tessellation (see the '2-D and 3-D shapes section' on page 23) is also useful to explore the covering of surfaces.
- The children can use the writing frame on resource page 128 to describe their predictions and findings.

NAME DATE

WHO IS RIGHT?

Class M have been studying kilometres, metres and centimetres. Here are some of the things they've said about their school. Four are right and four are wrong.

■ Put a ✓ or a ✗ under each statement.

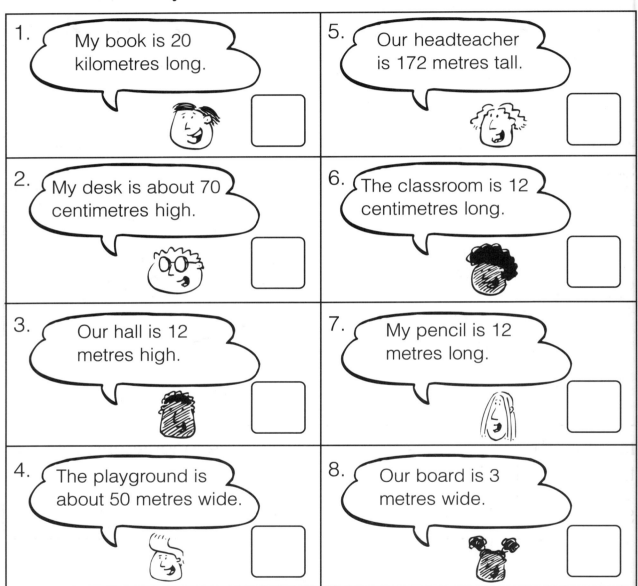

1. My book is 20 kilometres long.	5. Our headteacher is 172 metres tall.
2. My desk is about 70 centimetres high.	6. The classroom is 12 centimetres long.
3. Our hall is 12 metres high.	7. My pencil is 12 metres long.
4. The playground is about 50 metres wide.	8. Our board is 3 metres wide.

Do your friends agree?

Make up some statements like these about other things in your school. Write them on the back of this sheet.

SEE 'SHOW ME THE LENGTH', PAGE 80.

NAME DATE

ALONG THE LINE

Set 1

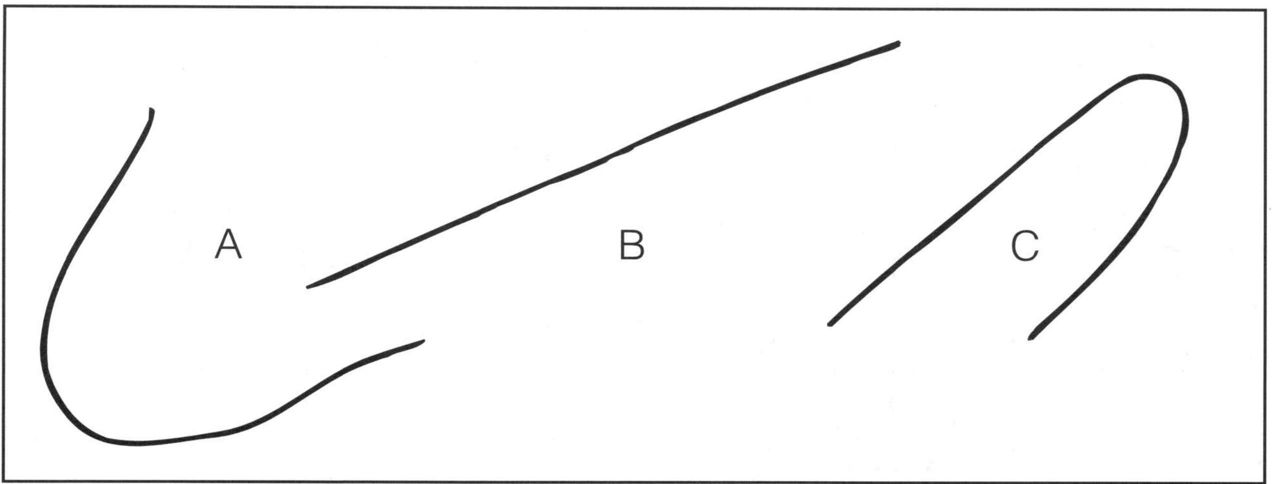

Set 2

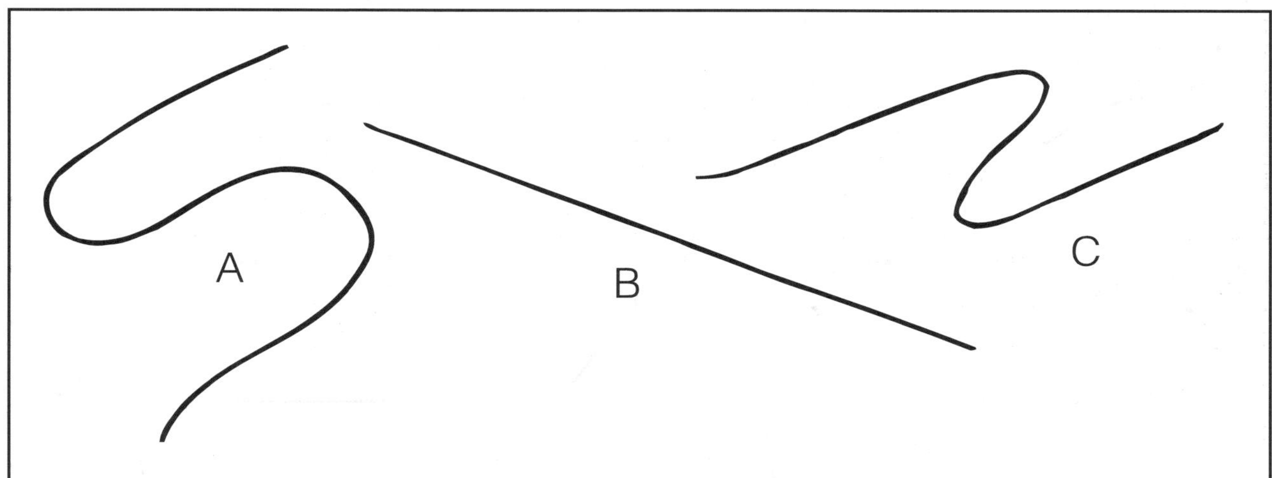

■ In each of these sets of lines, which is the longest and which is the shortest?

Set 1:

Set 2:

On the back of the sheet, draw straight and wavy lines that are (a) 10cm long and (b) 15cm long. Underneath, write an instruction for measuring the wavy lines.

SEE 'ALL THE WAY ROUND', PAGE 88.

LENGTH & AREA

NAME DATE

PERIMETER CHALLENGE

- Which one of these shapes do you think has the longest perimeter?
- Which one do you think has the shortest perimeter?
- Now measure and see.

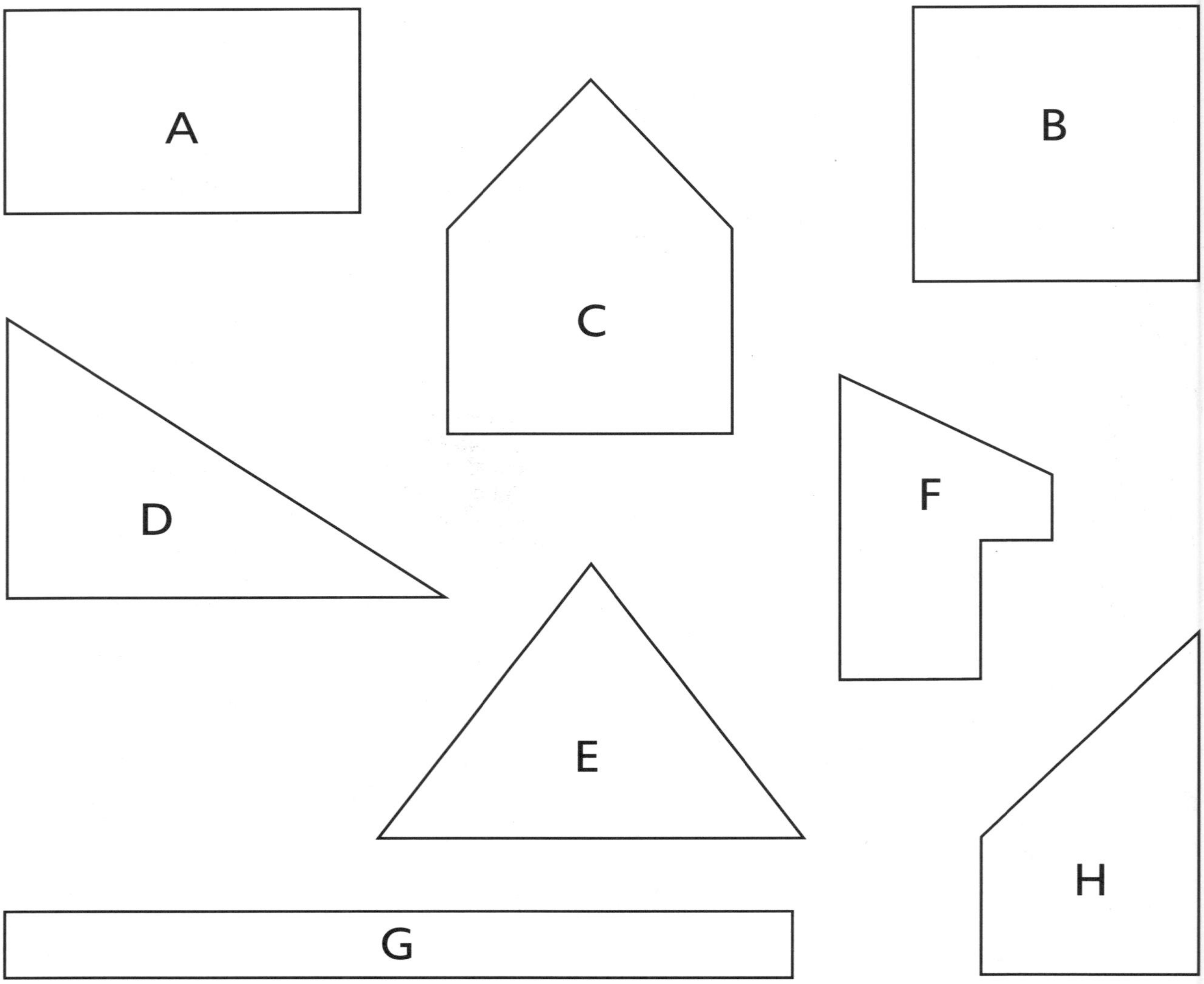

A

B

C

D

F

E

H

G

Were you right? ______ Does your partner agree? ________

Which perimeters were easy to measure? Which were more tricky?

SEE 'MEASURE THE EDGE', PAGE 88.

NAME DATE

HALF A SQUARE

■ Find some more ways to halve the area of this square. Can you halve all the squares in different ways?

Compare your designs with your friend's. Which designs is it easy to see are half the area? Which designs is it harder to be sure about?

SEE 'THE LARGEST PIECE', PAGE 83.

NAME DATE

HOW MUCH IS COVERED?

■ Find the number of squares shaded in each picture.

A

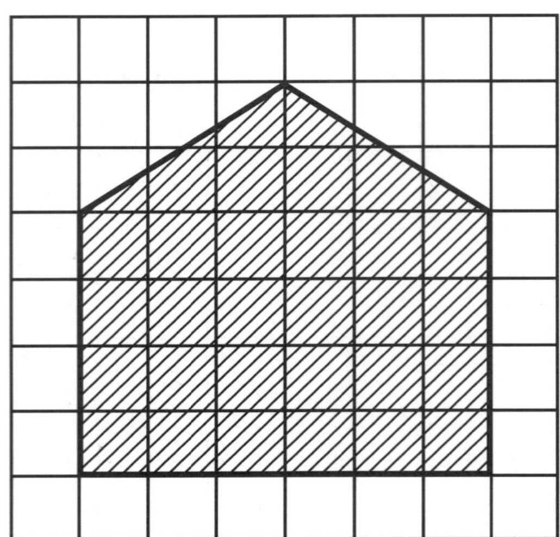

_______ squares

B

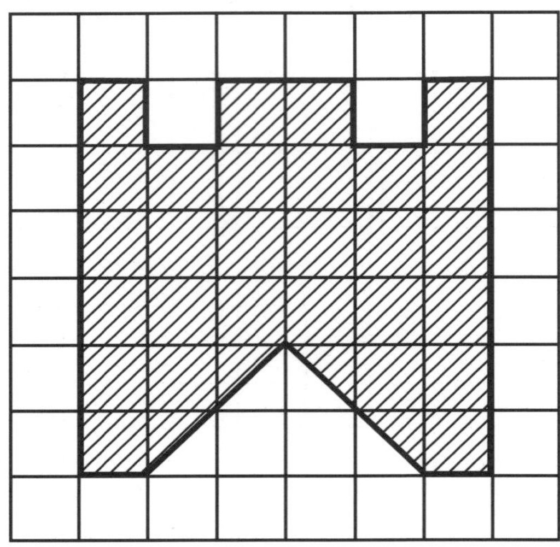

_______ squares

C

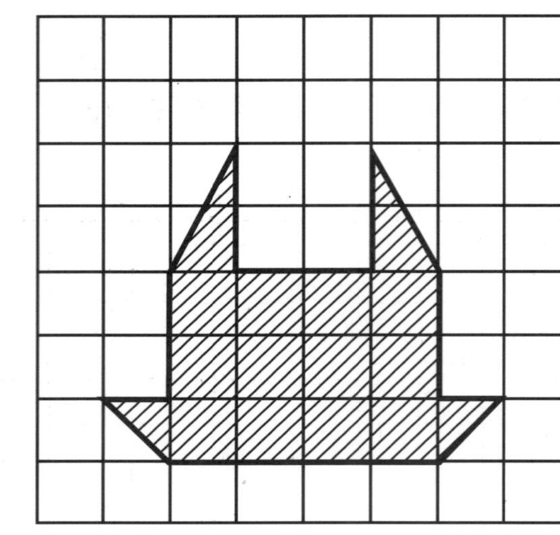

_______ squares

D

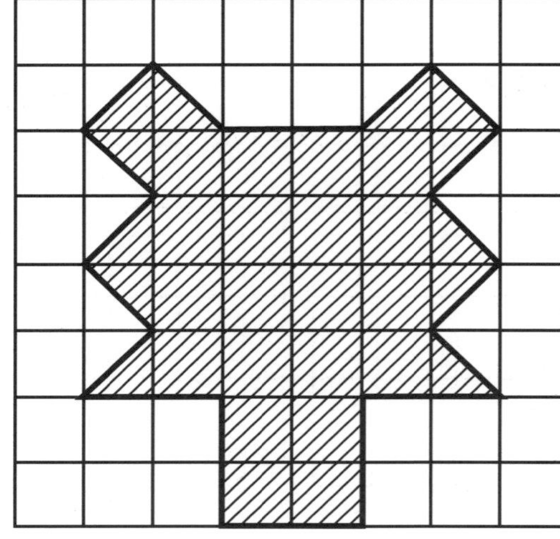

_______ squares

■ Use squared paper to draw three different pictures covering 26 squares, 19 squares and 32 squares respectively.

On the back of this sheet, write down what you do when part of a square is covered – how do you decide whether to count it or not?

SEE 'MEASURE YOUR HAND', PAGE 84.

NAME DATE

PERIMETER AND AREA

■ Find the area and perimeter of each of these rectangles. What do you notice?

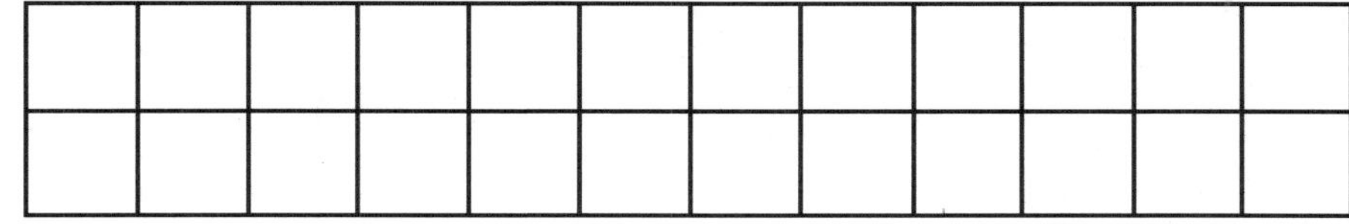

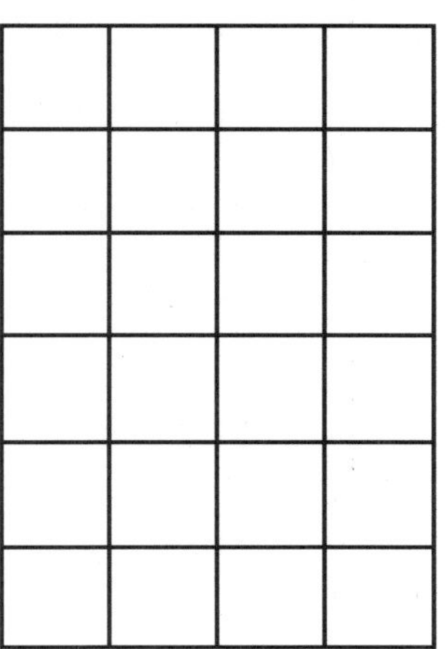

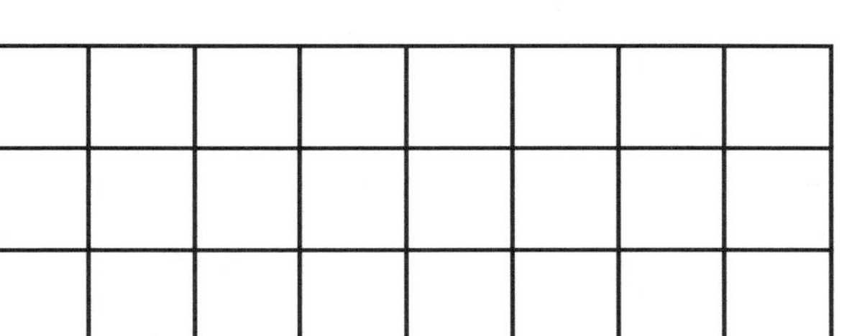

■ Now draw two rectangles on the squared paper below: one 6cm × 3cm and the other 9cm × 2cm.

■ Which will have the larger area? Which will have the larger perimeter? Predict and then check.

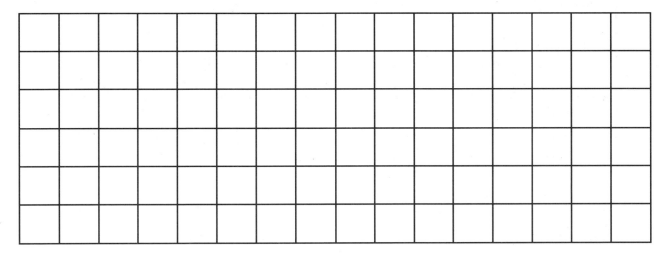

Use 1cm squared paper to try again with these rectangles: 12cm × 3cm, 9cm × 4cm and 6cm × 6cm.

What do you notice?

SEE 'FIVE SQUARES', PAGE 85.

KEY IDEAS

- Understanding mass as a measure of the quantity of an object.
- Understanding capacity as a measure of volume (usually liquid), related to how much 3-D space an object occupies.
- Using standard units (grams and kilograms, litres and millilitres).
- Being able to read a variety of scales for each measure.
- Estimating (using standard and non-standard units); building up a sense of each measure.

Children at this age need to spend time consolidating their practical experiences of mass and capacity, developing confidence with the language of each measure, and beginning to use a variety of different scales.

Mass and capacity are both measures of how much of something there is. In different ways, each of these measures is more complex than length. I can look at two strips of paper and see which is the longer, making a simple direct comparison between them. To compare the masses of two objects directly, I need to hold them: I cannot rely on a visual perception alone. Even then, I can only be sure which is heavier if there is a large difference between the masses; to be totally sure, I need to make the comparison using a balance or scales.

Understanding **transitivity** is important for judging the relative mass of different objects. This is the idea that if A is heavier than B and B is heavier than C, then A must be heavier than C. Research shows that around the age of six to eight, children are able to develop a confident understanding of this concept (they do not need to know its name!) and to apply it to a range of different measuring attributes.

In judging the relative capacity of two containers, I need to take account of their dimensions. This is not always easy to do – for example, if comparing two different-shaped bottles.

The understanding of each of these measures is linked to the Piagetian concept of **conservation**: children need to understand that an object can retain its mass and volume even when its dimensions are altered. If a lump of Plasticine is squashed or stretched, the mass and volume remain the same since the 'amount' of the substance is unchanged.

For each of these measures, children need to build up a sense of relative size. They need to be aware of what a mass of 1 kilogram or 100 grams feels like, and what familiar objects might be close in mass to each of those amounts. Similarly, they need to build up an idea of 1 litre or 100 millilitres. Only metric units should be used in the classroom at this stage, though the children may be familar with ounces, pounds, stones and pints from home.

BY THE END OF Y3/P4, MOST CHILDREN SHOULD BE ABLE TO:

- read and begin to write the vocabulary related to mass and capacity (such as 'weighs', 'balances', 'holds')
- measure and compare using standard units (kg, g, l, ml)
- know the relationship between kilograms and grams, and between litres and millilitres
- suggest suitable units and simple measuring equipment (such as jugs or balances) to estimate or measure mass and capacity
- record estimates and measurements
- suggest objects to measure using each unit.

BY THE END OF Y4/P5, MOST CHILDREN SHOULD BE ABLE TO:

- use, read and write standard metric units, including their abbreviations
- use the relationships between units (including converting between them)
- tell you the equivalent of one half, one quarter, three quarters and one tenth of 1kg and 1 litre in g and ml
- suggest suitable units and measuring equipment to estimate or measure mass or capacity
- record estimates and measurements to a suitable and increasing degree of accuracy.

SOME COMMON MISCONCEPTIONS AND STRATEGIES FOR CORRECTING THEM

MASS AND WEIGHT

The mass of a body is the amount of 'stuff' in it. Its weight is the force of gravity acting on it. A body will have the same mass on the Earth and on the Moon, but its weight will be different because the force of gravity is less on the Moon.

The difference between mass and weight is too technical for seven- to nine-year-olds, but they should be encouraged to use 'mass', which is the technically correct term.

USING UNITS

The system of prefixes used in the metric system makes the differences between the relative sizes of units less obvious than if they had entirely different names. Children are more likely to confuse 25g with 25kg than to confuse 20 ounces with 20 tons.

Reinforce the distinction between g and kg through activities which lead the children to visualize and discuss them (as in photocopiable page 111).

'LARGER IS HEAVIER'

Children often confuse **size** with **mass**. Because of the prime importance of visual perception (and possibly because of earlier work on measuring length), children often assume that a larger object is heavier.

This misconception can be dispelled by including large light objects (such as an empty cereal box) alongside small heavy objects (such as a stapler) in a range of objects that the children are experimenting with. Giving the children full and empty sealed identical packets will help to underline this point.

HEAVY OR HEAVIER?

Comparative terms are purely relative: if one object is heavier than another, that does not make it 'heavy' in any other context. Six feathers are six times heavier than one feather, but still light compared to a tin of beans. Extend the comparison suggested above by including several of any particular object.

READING SCALES

A range of different weighing scales and measuring cylinders are available, and children must learn to use a variety of these. If they assume that each graduation represents one unit (as with an infant ruler), they may just count the divisions and ignore the scale. For example, they may read this as 4ml of water:

Emphasize that they must **always** read the scale when measuring accurately.

MASSES OF FRUIT

Whole class, then groups
40 minutes

AIM
To develop the vocabulary of comparison for mass.

WHAT YOU WILL NEED
A range of different fruits (at least four, including some that are similar in size but different in mass), pan balances, a vocabulary list for display –**heavier, heaviest, lighter, lightest**.

WHAT TO DO
Show the children the fruits and ask them to discuss in pairs which they think will be the heaviest, the next heaviest and so on. Ask pairs to feed back: *does everyone agree?* Ask the children to justify their choices. Now ask them to suggest a way of finding out for sure. They may suggest holding two fruits, one in each hand. Emphasize that there is a limit to how accurate this can be. You might like to suggest that they hold the two fruits in identical bags to make comparison easier (see *Developing Shape, Space and Measures with 5–7 year olds* by Ros Leather).

Introduce a pan balance. Ask the children to suggest how this might help. Demonstrate what happens when a fruit is put in each pan. Go through the fruits, weighing one against another. Ask the children whether it is necessary to do this for every pair; tease out their understanding of transitivity (see 'Key ideas', page 96).

When the order of fruits (heaviest to lightest) has been established, the children should work (together or in groups) with further sets of fruits. Alternatively, they could use sets of stationery items (adhesive tape, sharpener, pencil, rubber and so on), books or mystery parcels. Insist that the children must write down their predictions for the order of mass of the objects **before** they use the balance. Giving different groups a greater or lesser number of items in their set makes the activity more or less complex.

DISCUSSION QUESTIONS
- *How can you tell which object is heavier?*
- *What can you say about this object compared to that one?*

ASSESSMENT
Do the children understand how to make the comparisons? Do they use the language of comparison in appropriate ways?

EXTENSIONS
- The children can try to find objects around the classroom with a mass greater or less than that of the objects they have, or a mass in between those of any pair of objects.
- They can use the writing frame on resource page 128 to reflect on this activity.

WHICH UNITS?

Whole class, then individuals or pairs
50 minutes

AIM
To choose appropriate units for different types of measure.

WHAT YOU WILL NEED
Photocopiable pages 110 and 111.

WHAT TO DO
Spend some time with the children brainstorming all the different units they can think of. Do they know what each is used for? There are two aspects to consider:

- *What type of unit – mass, capacity or length?*
- *What scale of unit – gram or kilogram, litre or millilitre, and so on?*

At this level, each of these aspects is best explained by a common-sense example. *I might drink 200ml of juice, but not 200 litres. Why not?*

The photocopiable sheets provide practice in this. Page 110 challenges the children to think about what units to use in different contexts. Make sure they understand that the numbers are correct: only the units have been mixed up.

Page 111 encourages them to think about the appropriate scale for units of mass and capacity in different contexts. The sheets could each provide a focus for a different session, or be used in the same session with older or more able children.

Encourage the children to see the humour in some of the obviously wrong answers – this is a good technique for reinforcing the correct ones. It is important to spend time reviewing children's answers with the whole class, as this is a good way to deal with any errors or misconceptions. The sheets could also be used for homework – the children can challenge their parents (who might find it difficult to deal with the metric units).

The answers to page 110 are: **1.** metres, **2.** litres, **3.** grams, **4.** centimetres, **5.** minutes, **6.** metres, **7.** grams, **8.** metres, **9.** grams. The answers to page 111 are: **1.** true, **2.** false, **3.** true, **4.** false, **5.** false, **6.** true, **7.** false, **8.** true.

DISCUSSION QUESTIONS
- *What are metres/litres/grams used for?*
- *What is a sensible unit to use for that?*
- *Why is that obviously wrong?*

ASSESSMENT
Can the children identify appropriate units for different aspects of measure? Do they use an appropriate scale within each unit?

EXTENSIONS
- See the further ideas suggested at the end of each sheet.
- You could make a class book or display of children's own statements or 'mixed-up units' stories.

MASS & CAPACITY

MORE OR LESS

Whole class, then groups of 4
50 minutes

AIM
To develop a sense of different standard masses.

WHAT YOU WILL NEED
A set of masses (1kg, 500g, 200g, 100g, 50g, 20g, 10g, 5g, 2g, 1g) per group; a number of 'real' objects such as books, pencil cases and grocery items (include some small 'heavy' items such as a stapler and some large 'light' items such as an empty cereal box); pan balances (one per group).

WHAT TO DO
Show the children a set of different masses. Pass them around and let the children pick them up and hold each mass. Ask them to describe how, for example, a 500g mass feels; how does it compare to, say, a 20g or a 1kg mass? Now ask for a volunteer, who should close his or her eyes. Choose a second child to select one of the masses and pass it to the first child, who has to guess which mass it is. Repeat with different children. (This warm-up can be repeated several times during other sessions.)

Now show the children the range of items you have prepared. Ask them to guess something that will be more than 100g but less than 200g. Show them how to check this using a pan balance, the chosen object and the two masses. If the object swings down with 100g but up with 200g, you have proved that its mass is between 100g and 200g. If the object is lighter or heavier than each of the masses, try with the next lighter/heavier mass.

Now give each group a set of masses and a range of different items (they can find extra ones around the classroom as the session progresses). Explain that the task is to find items that are more than or less than particular masses. You could reproduce a table like the one below for them to record their results in, or let older or more confident children devise their own method of recording. (The class computer may be useful here.)

In the plenary session, repeat the 'eyes closed' game with different items instead of the masses. Can the children make a sensible estimate of the mass of each object?

Mass between...	Item
1g and 2g	
2g and 5g	
5g and 10g	
10g and 20g	
20g and 50g	
50g and 100g	
100g and 200g	
200g and 500g	
500g and 1kg	

DISCUSSION QUESTIONS
- *Are large things heavier than small things?*
- *Was it easier to estimate the masses of heavy or light items?*
- *Which items surprised you?*

ASSESSMENT
Do the children demonstrate/develop a good sense of the relative size of different masses?

EXTENSIONS
- The children can find the exact mass of an object by using a number of masses to balance it. For example, an object weighing 153g will be balanced exactly by masses of 100g, 50g, 2g and 1g. The recording table could have an extra two columns (headed 'Masses to balance' and 'Exact mass') for showing this.
- Photocopiable page 106 can be used to consolidate the numerical relationships between different masses (in grams). Link this to work on addition of three-digit numbers. The answers are: **1.** 50g, 20g and 2g. **2.** 200g, 100g and 10g. **3.** 500g, 20g and 5g. **4.** 20g, 2g and 1g. **5.** 50g, 5g, 2g and 1g. **6.** 500g, 200g, 50g and 2g. **7.** 200g, 100g, 50g and 10g. **8.** 50g, 20g, 10g, 5g and 1g.

WHAT'S THE MASS?

Groups
50 minutes

AIMS
To estimate mass using standard and non-standard units, using the concept of 'range'. To use a variety of weighing scales.

WHAT YOU WILL NEED
A collection of things to weigh (for example, grocery items, fruits, 3-D shapes, stationery items); non-standard units to weigh with (conkers, cubes, marbles); pan balances; weighing scales of various types; a range of masses.

WHAT TO DO
This activity follows a similar pattern to the activities in the 'Length and Area' section: 'How long? (1)' and 'How long? (2)' (pages 80 and 87). Ask the children to work in groups, finding the mass of each of a set of items. Choose one of the following approaches (or use all three for a progressive series of lessons):

1. The children use a pan balance with non-standard units. For example:
- *How many conkers balance a tin of baked beans?*
- *How many cubes balance a pencil case?*

Note the difference between **uniform** or regular units (cubes, marbles) and **non-uniform** units (conkers). A possible table for recording is shown below. (The class computer could be useful here.)

2. The children use a pan balance with a standard set of masses.
3. Introduce the use of a weighing scale. The children estimate and then measure the masses, using standard units.

DISCUSSION QUESTIONS
- *What is the most/least anyone thinks the answer might be?*
- *Can we narrow the range a little?*
- *What objects do you like using to measure mass? Why?*

ASSESSMENT
Do the children appreciate the difference between uniform and non-uniform measures of mass? Can they develop sensible estimates using the 'range' method? Can they measure objects accurately using a pan balance or a weighing scale?

EXTENSIONS
- The children can use the writing frame on resource page 128 to reflect on this activity.
- The activity 'What's in the bag?' (page 102) provides further experience in using standard weighing scales.
- Photocopiable page 107 provides more experience in reading scales (to 0.5kg and then 50g divisions). The answers are: 3kg, 1.5kg, 4.5kg, 2kg, 0.5kg, 5kg, 400g, 700g, 350g, 950g, 500g, 50g.

Object	Measured with	Estimate: Minimum	Estimate: Maximum	Actual number
Pencil case	Conkers			
Tin of beans	Marbles			

MAKE THE MASS

Whole class, then groups
50 minutes

AIM
To develop a more exact sense of standard masses.

WHAT YOU WILL NEED
A set of masses (1kg, 500g, 200g, 100g, 50g, 20g, 10g, 5g, 2g, 1g) per group; Plasticine or play dough; pan balances.

WHAT TO DO

Review the standard set of masses. You can play the 'Eyes closed' game (see 'More or less', page 100) as a warm-up.

Ask the children to use Plasticine or play dough to make different masses that are not available in the standard set. They should work in groups to devise a way, using the pan balance and the standard set of masses, to create Plasticine 'standard masses' for 15g, 25g, 30g and 40g.

DISCUSSION QUESTIONS

- *How can you make a mass of 15g... 25g...?*
- *Was it easy or hard to choose the right amount of Plasticine?*

ASSESSMENT

Can the children make their own sets of accurate masses? Test their masses to check.

VARIATION

- Younger or less experienced children can make their own set of 'standard masses' from Plasticine.

EXTENSIONS

- The children can use their sets of plasticine masses to weigh a range of items.
- They can swap sets of masses and test them.

WHAT'S IN THE BAG?

Groups
50 minutes

AIMS

To use standard units of mass, including the relationship between grams and kilograms. To use a weighing scale.

WHAT YOU WILL NEED

Carrier bags (one per group) with a variety of items in each (either grocery items or books), of a total mass of at least 2kg per bag; one set of weighing scales (for individual items) per group; bathroom scales (with the traditional dial).

WHAT TO DO

Show the bathroom scales to the children. Explain that it is useful for weighing heavy items (as well as themselves), such as packed bags before a trip. Introduce the unit 'kilogram' and explain its relationship to grams: there are 1000 grams in 1 kilogram. Note that, with the bathroom scales, the lack of fine divisions between kilograms makes it impossible to measure an exact number of grams.

Ask the groups to use the bathroom scales to find the total mass of their packed bag, then unpack it and weigh each item separately using a pan balance or classroom scales in grams. They should record the masses, find the total, then convert it to kilograms and check that it matches the mass of the packed bag.

DISCUSSION QUESTIONS

- *Why is it more accurate to weigh each item individually?*
- *Did you find approximately the same total mass both times?*
- *When might you use kilograms rather than grams?*

ASSESSMENT

Can the children use the different scales with accuracy? Can they use the relationship between grams and kilograms in simple calculations?

EXTENSIONS

- The children can use different types of bag. A heavier bag (such as a leather holdall) will distort the comparison because its own mass is included when the bathroom scales is used, but not when the items are weighed individually. Do the children realize this discrepancy? (This idea is explored further in the activity 'Weighing water', page 105).
- Photocopiable page 108 provides practice in converting masses from kilograms (decimals) to grams and vice versa, and from litres (decimals) to millilitres and vice versa. Photocopiable page 107 provides practice in reading weighing scales (for answers, see page 101).

HOW MANY SPOONFULS?

Whole class, then groups
50 minutes

AIMS
To understand capacity as 'filling containers'. To consider the relative capacity of a range of containers. To solve a problem involving capacity.

WHAT YOU WILL NEED
A variety of open containers (such as cups, beakers, jam jars, buckets); smaller items such as spoons, scoops, small beakers; water. Each group will need one spoon or scoop, one jar or cup, and one larger bucket.

WHAT TO DO
Hold up two beakers of contrasting capacity. Ask the children: *Which holds more? How many times more? How could you find out?* Demonstrate how to do this by filling the smaller container and pouring its contents into the larger, then repeating until the larger container is full.

Now show children three contrasting items such as a bucket, cup and spoon. Ask them how they could find out how many spoonfuls will fill the bucket. Obviously it would be tedious to do this in reality. A solution (which the children should be prompted to suggest) is to fill the cup with spoonfuls, then fill the bucket with cupfuls. If 40 spoonfuls fill the cup and 15 cupfuls fill the bucket, then the number of spoonfuls needed to fill the bucket is $40 \times 15 = 600$. (If the numbers are awkward, use a calculator for this part.)

Group the children and give each group a set of three different items (such as a spoon, a cup and a bucket). They should experiment with these to establish relationships as in the demonstration, and draw up a table to show their estimates and results. They will also have to devise a method of tallying to keep track of their count.

Bring the class back together to review their findings. Focus on how the measurements were made, what was discovered, and any discrepancies or errors that have arisen.

DISCUSSION QUESTIONS
- *How can you find out how many of these will fill that?*
- *How accurate is your answer?*
- *Were you surprised by how many were needed?*

ASSESSMENT
Are the children able to use the relative sizes of the containers to find a sensible solution?

VARIATIONS
- Pose the question the other way around: *How many times can this bucket of water fill that small cup?*
- The children can use a set of four (or even five) containers of different capacity. How many of the smallest container will fill the largest? They will have to decide which container(s) to use as the intermediate(s).

WHICH HOLDS MOST?

Whole class, then groups
40 minutes

AIMS
To measure the capacity of a range of containers. To estimate and measure using standard units of capacity.

WHAT YOU WILL NEED
A range of containers (such as bowls, cups, beakers, jam jars, bottles); measuring cylinders; water. Each group will need a contrasting set of containers including something wide and short (such as a bowl) and something tall and thin (such as a shampoo bottle). Remove or cover any labels stating the containers' capacity.

WHAT TO DO
Show the children a measuring cylinder and discuss the scale along the side. Remind them that the standard units of capacity are litres and millilitres, and that there are 1000ml in 1 litre. Fill one measuring cylinder up to 100ml to show what that looks like, and show some containers of a specific capacity (such as a 1 litre or 0.5 litre lemonade bottle).

Now tell the children that their task is to estimate the capacity of a range of containers. Give each group a variety of containers. They should examine these and predict their relative capacity, then list them in order from the smallest to the largest capacity. They should then estimate the number of millilitres or litres that each contains (they could use the 'range' method described elsewhere). Finally, they should use measuring cylinders to confirm the capacity of each and their relative order.

Note that for some items (such as a bowl) it is easier to pour water from the measuring cylinder into the container than the other way round. Using this method, they should put (say) 500ml of water in the measuring cylinder, pour carefully into the bowl until it is full, then note how much water is left in the measuring cylinder. Subtracting the number of ml remaining in the measuring cylinder from 500 will give the capacity of the bowl.

DISCUSSION QUESTIONS

- *Do taller containers hold more?*
- *What's the best way to find out how much that holds?*
- *Did you get the order right? How can you be sure?*
- *Did any of the containers surprise you?*

ASSESSMENT

Are the children able to order the containers by estimated capacity? Are they able to make sensible estimates of the capacity of the containers?

VARIATION

Increase/reduce the number of items per group, and provide containers whose capacity is harder/easier to estimate.

EXTENSION

- The children can use the writing frame on resource page 128 to reflect on this activity.
- Photocopiable page 109 provides further practice in reading scales on measuring cylinders.

16 CUBES

Whole class, then groups
40 minutes

AIM

To understand the conservation of volume.

WHAT YOU WILL NEED

Interlocking cubes, weighing scales, rulers.

WHAT TO DO

Prepare two or three examples of small figures made from 16 interlocking cubes, with different shape characteristics (for example, one tall and thin, another long and thin and a third short and squat – these could be models of a tower, a lizard and a house). The models could be either 3-D or 2-D. Ask the children what these figures have in common, and what is different about them, in terms of various measures. For example:

- *Which figure is the heaviest?*
- *Which is the longest?*
- *Which takes up the most space?*

Now distribute cubes to each group. Within each group, each child should make a different 16-cube model. They should then compare their figures as before, making other comparisons as appropriate.

In a final discussion, encourage the children to recognize that all the 16-cube models have the same mass and volume.

DISCUSSION QUESTIONS

- *Do all the figures have the same mass? Why?*
- *Does the longest/tallest/widest figure take up the most space?*
- *How can you show that these two have the same mass/take up the same space?*

ASSESSMENT

Do the children understand the relationships between the different aspects of measure? Do they understand that mass and volume are conserved when parts of a 3-D shape are rearranged?

VARIATIONS

- The children can use more or fewer cubes.

EXTENSIONS

- The children can make a scale model of one of their figures, using twice as many cubes. *Is it twice as heavy? Is it twice as long?*
- They can use the writing frame on resource page 128 to reflect on what they have learnt from this activity.

WEIGHING WATER

Whole class, then groups
50 minutes

AIMS

To find the mass of a given volume of liquid. To use standard units of mass and capacity.

WHAT YOU WILL NEED

Measuring cylinders, weighing scales, jars with lids, water, paper, pencils.

WHAT TO DO

Ask the children to discuss in pairs how they might find out the mass of a given volume of water (such as 100ml or 500ml). Then ask for their suggestions. The point to draw out in discussion is that because the water will have to be weighed in a container, they will have to weigh that first, then weigh the container with water in it, then subtract the container's mass.

Ask each group to find the masses of two particular volumes of water. In order to encourage accuracy in making measurements, it is a good idea to suggest volumes of water that have a clear relationship, such as 100ml and 200ml or 250ml and 500m – in each case, the children should find that the latter has twice the mass of the former. They will thus have an immediate way of checking whether their results are accurate.

Give the children a suitable amount of time to measure, calculate and record; then bring the class back together to discuss their findings, focusing on the relationships they have discovered.

DISCUSSION QUESTIONS

- *How can you find out what water weighs?*
- *What can you say about the mass of 1ml/1 litre of water?*

ASSESSMENT

Do the children make sensible suggestions for methods of weighing water? Do they carry out their work systematically, making and recording accurate measurements? Do they make a clear distinction between units of capacity (litres and millilitres) and units of mass (grams and kilograms)?

EXTENSIONS

- Do all liquids have the same mass for a given volume? The children could repeat the activity with fruit juice, lemonade, cooking oil and so on. Different groups could work with different liquids. This links to science work on the concept of density.
- What if the water has something dissolved in it, such as salt, sugar or coffee granules: how does this affect the mass of a given volume? (It will be greater than for pure water.) This links to science work on dissolving.
- The children can use the writing frame on resource page 128 to reflect on what they have learnt.
- Photocopiable page 108 provides an opportunity to practise reading and writing units of mass and capacity.

NAME DATE

MAKE IT BALANCE

■ Which of these masses would you use to balance the parcels? You only have one of each mass.

1. 72g

2.

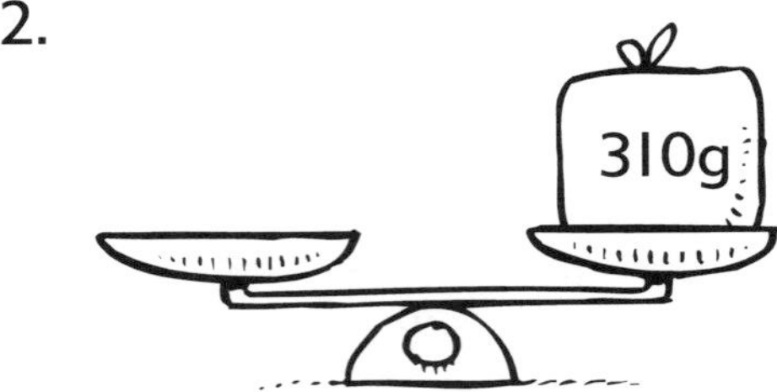

3. 525g

4.

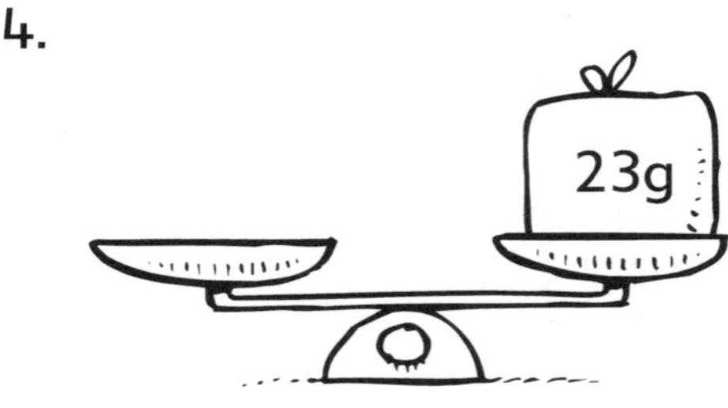

5. 58g

6.

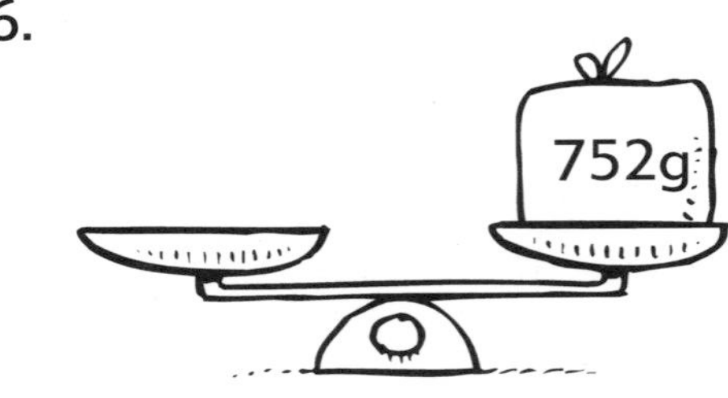

7. 360g

8.

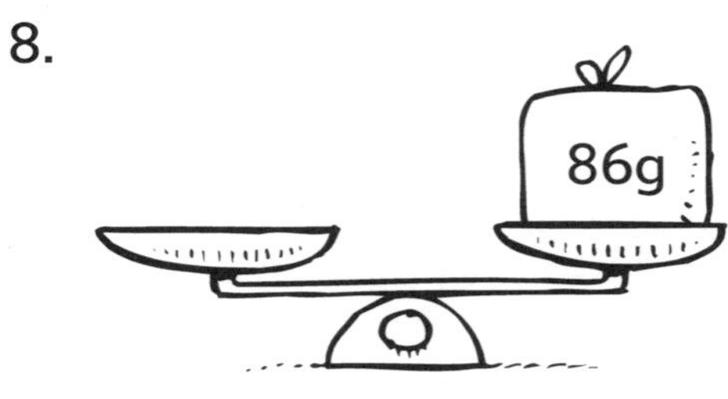

Check with a friend. Do you have the same answers?

Now imagine you have two of each mass. Can you balance each parcel in a new way? Draw on the back of the sheet.

SEE 'MORE OR LESS', PAGE 100.

NAME DATE

READ THE MASS

■ Write down what mass is shown on each set of scales. Don't forget the units!

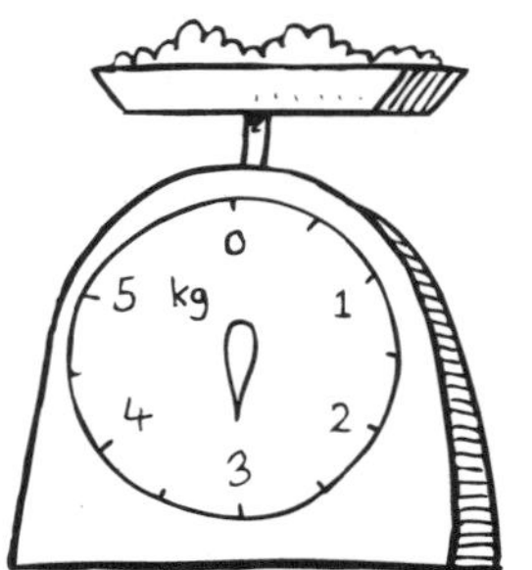
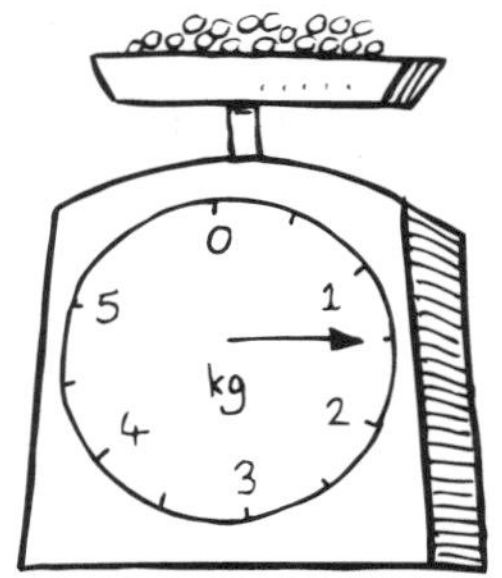
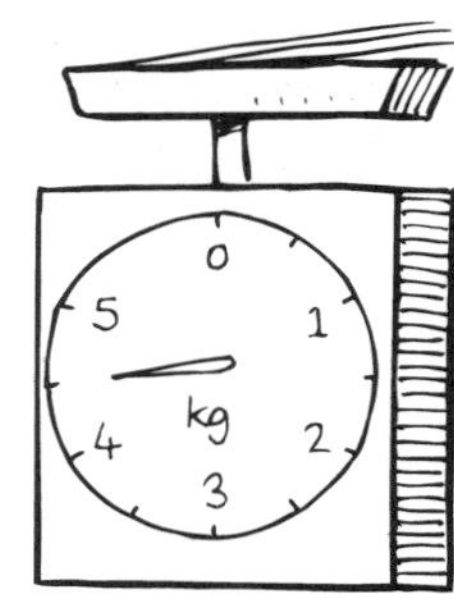

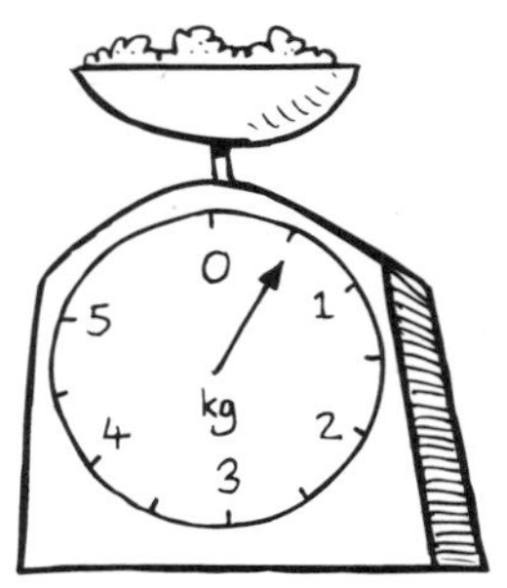

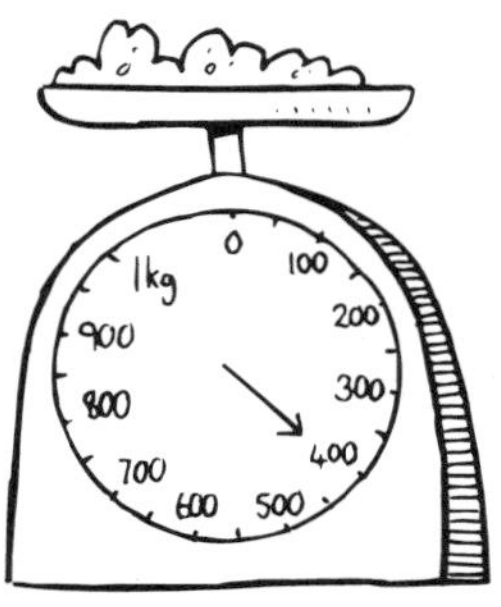
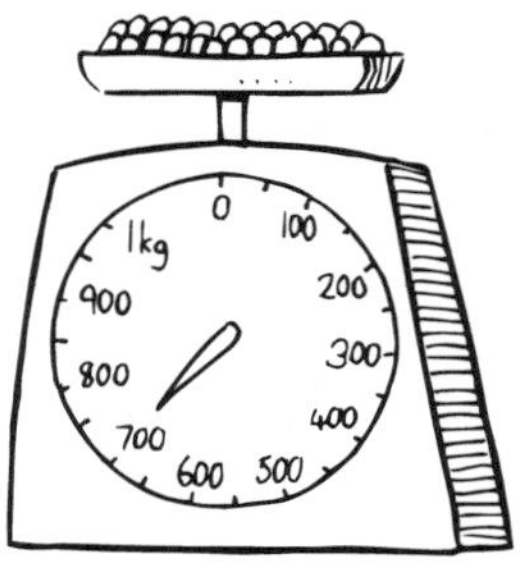
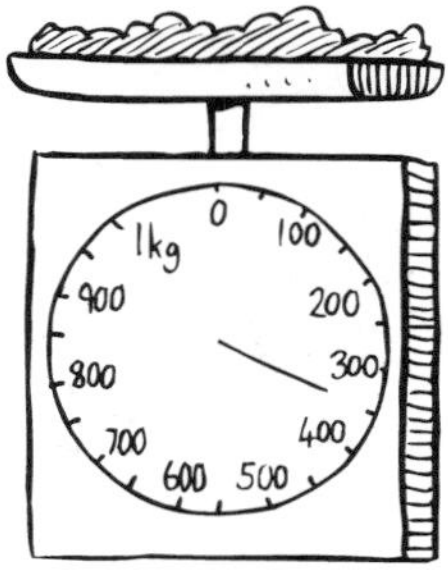
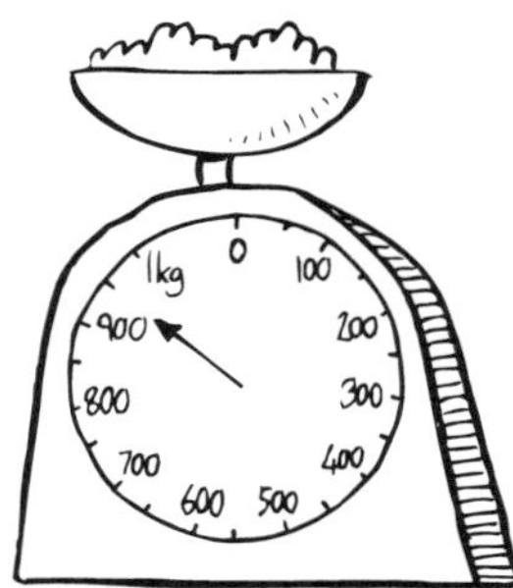
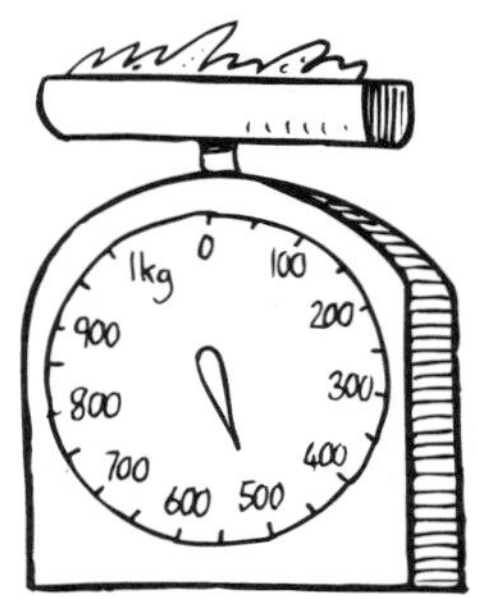

Check your answers with a friend. Do you agree?

SEE 'WHAT'S THE MASS?', PAGE 101, AND 'WHAT'S IN THE BAG?', PAGE 102.

NAME DATE

EXPLORING UNITS

■ **Remember:** 1kg = 1000g and 1 litre = 1000ml

A 2.645kg = 2kg 645g

Rewrite these in the same way:

1. 4.382kg =
2. 5.247kg =
3. 7.399kg =
4. 0.675kg =
5. 8.888kg =
6. 4.035kg =

B 7893g = 7.893kg

Rewrite these in the same way:

1. 4567g =
2. 5495g =
3. 7777g =
4. 8095g =
5. 359g =
6. 7905g =

C 4.745 litres = 4l 745ml

Rewrite these in the same way:

1. 7.955 litres =
2. 6.352 litres =
3. 7.894 litres =
4. 0.854 litres =
5. 6.789 litres =
6. 8.042 litres =

D 6794ml = 6.794 litres

Rewrite these in the same way:

1. 2876ml =
2. 9292ml =
3. 3672ml =
4. 586ml =
5. 6096ml =
6. 2707ml =

Write a note for a friend who has been away from school, explaining how to change kg to g and litres to ml.

SEE 'WHAT'S IN THE BAG?', PAGE 102, AND 'WEIGHING WATER', PAGE 105.

NAME DATE

HOW FULL?

■ Write down the volume of water in each container.

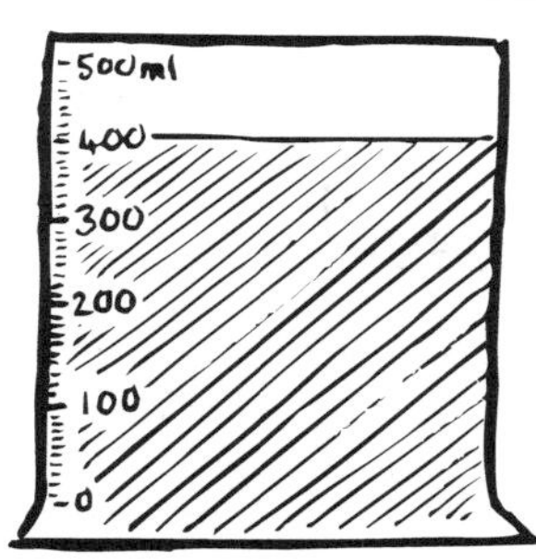

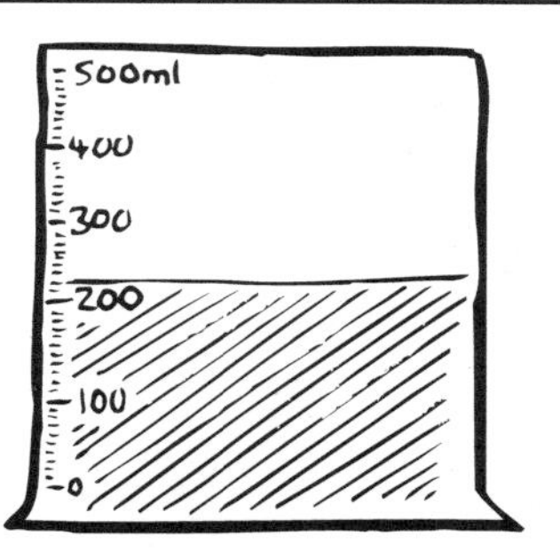

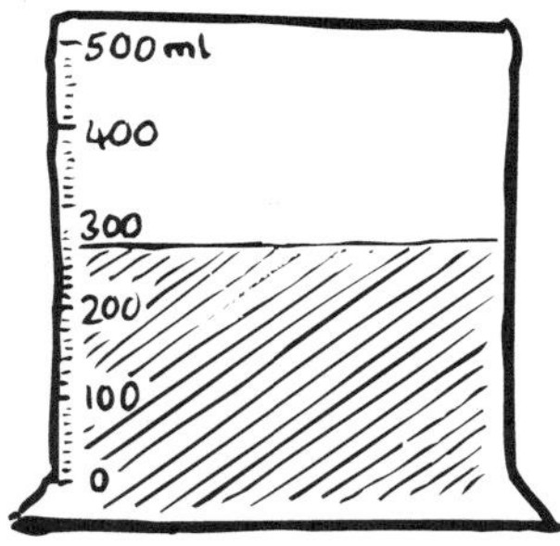

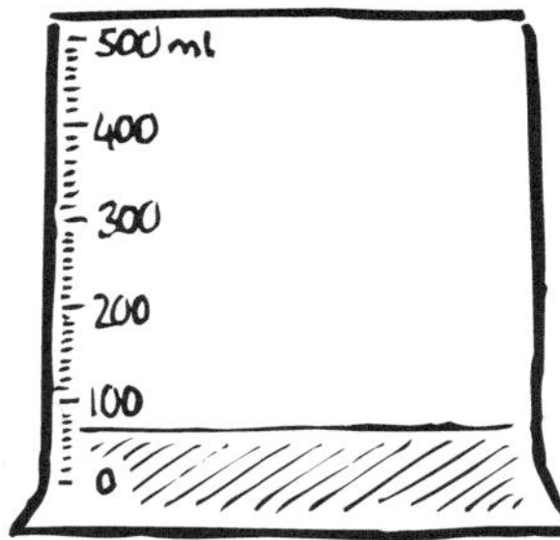

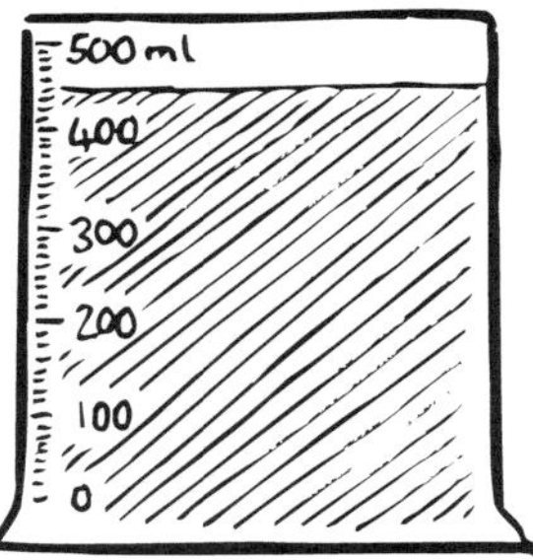

Check your answers with a friend. Do you agree?

SEE 'WHICH HOLDS MOST?', PAGE 103.

NAME DATE

MASS & CAPACITY

A TALL STORY

William walked 400 grams to the shops. He bought a 2 metre bottle of lemonade and 40 litres of jelly babies. His sister bought a great comic – it was 25 litres wide. It took her 30 grams to read it.

In the afternoon they went to the park, where there was a pond 2 kilograms deep. They brought 200 metres of bread to feed the ducks. Afterwards they went on the slide, which was 5 litres high. Then on the way home, they bought ice cream – the cones weighed 100 centimetres. Yummy!

■ In the story above, the numbers are correct – but the units are all wrong! What should the real units be?

William's walk: __________

Volume of lemonade: __________

Mass of jelly babies: __________

Width of comic: __________

Time taken to read comic: __________

Depth of pond: __________

Mass of bread: __________

Height of slide: __________

Mass of ice cream cone: __________

On the back of this sheet, write your own 'mixed-up units' story to try out with your friends.

SEE 'WHICH UNITS?', PAGE 99.

NAME DATE

TRUE OR FALSE?

Class M have been studying kilograms, grams, litres and millilitres. Here are some of the things they've said about their families. Four statements are right and four are wrong.

■ Under each statement, put a ✓ or a ✗.

1. Mum put 30 litres of petrol in our car. ☐	2. I use 40 millilitres of water in the bath. ☐
3. My brother puts 200 millilitres of milk on his cornflakes. ☐	4. Dad gave me 5 litres of medicine when I was sick. ☐
5. My baby brother weighs 7 grams. ☐	6. Our family eat 4 kilograms of potatoes a week. ☐
7. Our car weighs 10 kilograms. ☐	8. My sister reckons a bag of crisps weighs around 35 grams. ☐

Does your friend agree?

On the back of this sheet, write some statements like these about other things in your house.

SEE 'WHICH UNITS?', PAGE 99.

KEY IDEAS

- Estimating the length of events.
- Using a clock face.
- Understanding a calendar.
- Linking analogue to digital clock times.
- Understanding simple timetables.

There are three aspects of time that children need to be confident with by the time they are eight or nine years old:

1. The passage of time. How long is one minute? How long is five minutes? Children need to build up a sense of time passing. This is more abstract than length or mass, since an 'amount' of time cannot be seen or felt. I can measure a line to find its length, then repeat to check; but once a period of time has passed, I cannot go back to check it – only move on and check another period of time later on.

2. The relationships between units. The wide variety of different units of time (seconds, minutes, hours, days, weeks, months, years) and the diverse relationships between these units (none of them follows the place value conventions of relationships between metric units) is a potential source of confusion, particularly when calculation of a period of time is necessary.

3. Telling the time on an analogue clock face. The last twenty years have seen a greatly increased use of digital time displays (on watches, videos, cookers and so on), and the tradition of a parent or grandparent teaching a child to 'tell the time' seems to have declined. This doesn't make teaching this skill any easier. Because the analogue clock face can often seen an abstract device to children, it is important to link the reading of clock times to real events during the day.

BY THE END OF Y3/P4, MOST CHILDREN SHOULD BE ABLE TO:

- read and begin to write vocabulary related to time (including **century, calendar, am, pm**)
- use the common units of time and know the relationships between them
- read the time to five minutes on a 12-hour analogue or digital clock
- suggest suitable units to estimate or measure times (for example, the time taken to boil an egg or the time left until an event)
- use a calendar
- use the terms **am** and **pm** and the notation 9.53
- solve problems involving multiples of 5 (minutes) in the context of analogue or digital times.

BY THE END OF Y4/P5, MOST CHILDREN SHOULD BE ABLE TO:

- use, read and write vocabulary related to time (including the days of the week, months and seasons)
- know how many days there are in each month of the year
- estimate and measure times using seconds, minutes and hours
- read the time on an analogue clock to the nearest minute
- read simple timetables and calculate using a calendar, converting between units as appropriate
- solve increasingly complex problems with more than one step, involving multiples of 5 (minutes) or the calculation of dates.

SOME COMMON MISCONCEPTIONS AND STRATEGIES FOR CORRECTING THEM

THE HOUR HAND

Although they may be confident in reading clock times, many children, when asked to draw hands on a clock face, will still draw the hour hand 'on the hour' regardless of the minutes past the hour. For example:

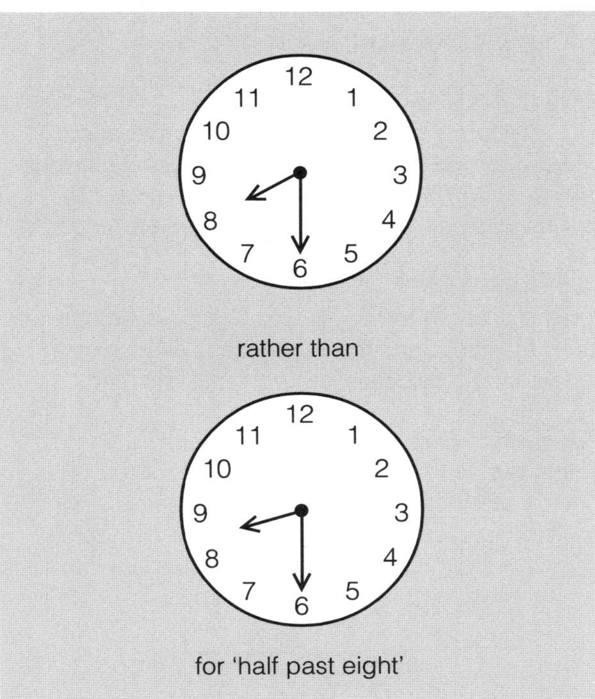

Ask the child to observe a real clock: the hour hand does not jerk suddenly from one hour to the next; it moves slowly and steadily around the dial.

TIMES 'TO THE HOUR'

Children often find it difficult to read a time like the above 'to the hour' ('twenty-five to three'). Not only do they have to deal with two scales (hours and minutes) on the same dial, they have to read one backwards and the other forwards. Reading a digital time 'to the hour' uses different skills. Children need to see many examples of analogue and digital clock faces with the time written alongside them for this to be reinforced.

CALCULATIONS WITH TIME

The non-metric nature of units of time often confuses children when they try to calculate with these units – particularly when questions are presented in a digital format. If the school assembly starts at 9.50 and lasts 20 minutes, when does it end? Many children will quite happily answer '9.70'.

Reminding the children that there are only sixty minutes in an hour is not enough: they need to return to the clock face to realize that, in the example given, the minute hand has passed the 12 and moved on into the next hour.

UNITS OF TIME

Whole class, then individuals
50 minutes

AIM
To understand the relationship between different units of time.

WHAT YOU WILL NEED
A large table showing the relationships between different units of time (the glossary on page 77 could be enlarged for this purpose), photocopiable page 118, calculators.

WHAT TO DO
Start with a quick quiz around the class, revising facts about the relationships between units; then display the table as a reminder.

Now ask the children how they might answer questions such as:

- *How many minutes are there in two hours?*
- *How many hours are there in two days?*
- *How many days are there in five weeks?*

They should realise that such questions require a simple multiplication. In some instances (such as the number of days in 43 weeks) where children may find the multiplication difficult, it might be appropriate to use a calculator. Talk through several questions of this kind with the class.

Give each child a copy of page 118. This activity sheet introduces an extension of the questions already considered: the children have to convert from one unit to another in order to compare two amounts of time. The children should complete the sheet individually.

Now review the answers with the whole class. Encourage them to explain their strategies for solving the problems.

DISCUSSION QUESTIONS
- *Can you put these units of time in order of size?*
- *How can you remember the relationship between these units? [What answers should they give?]*
- *How can you tell which period of time is longer?*

ASSESSMENT
Do the children remember the relationships between units of time? Can they use these relationships to make simple calculations?

EXTENSION
Page 118 can be used as a template for further sheets of similar questions. Questions involving multiple calculations (for example, the number of seconds in an hour or minutes in a week) will provide a challenge for more confident pupils.

A DAY IN THE LIFE

Whole class, then individuals
50 minutes

AIMS
To sequence events. To match digital to analogue clock times.

WHAT YOU WILL NEED
Card clocks (at least one per pair of children), photocopiable page 121.

WHAT TO DO
Revise the use of the clock face with the children by giving out card clocks and calling out various times for the children to move the hands to. Your choice of times will depend on the children's experience; but it is worth starting with easier times (whole hours, half past, quarter past and quarter to) in order to build their confidence. Next, try the other 'past times': ten past, twenty past and so on. Finally, look at 'times to': five to, twenty to and so on.

Now ask the children to name events that happen during an ordinary day. Scribe a list of all their ideas on the board or flip chart, then ask the children to put them into a sequence. Rewrite the events in sequence, beginning with 'Waking up in the morning' and ending with 'Going to sleep at night'. Include the various events of the school day – assembly, literacy and numeracy lessons, break, lunch time, home time – as well as after-school clubs, play centre or favourite TV programmes.

Now ask the children to agree on what times these events occur, as well as which events are in the morning (before midday) and which are in the afternoon (after midday). For some events (such as getting up in the morning), the time may vary between different children. As you go through the times of the day that the events occur, the children should use their clock faces to model each time. Write up the times in 12-hour digital format (for example, 4.45) beside the events. Through discussion, compare the different ways in which a time can be stated: '4.45', '4.45pm', 'quarter to five in the afternoon'.

Now give out copies of page 121 and ask the children to fill in events from the day in sequence, writing the times digitally in the boxes and drawing hands on the clocks. They can take all their events and times from the board, or create their own version.

DISCUSSION QUESTIONS
- *How can you show me [using clock faces] half past three... quarter past seven... quarter to one?*
- *What things happen in the morning... evening... afternoon?*
- *What order do these things happen in?*

ASSESSMENT
Can the children sequence the events of the day correctly? Do they have a good sense of when different events occur during the day? Can they place hands on the clock faces correctly to represent particular times? Can they convert analogue to digital times and vice versa?

VARIATION
Photocopiable page 121 allows for the recording of nine events; for some children, it might be appropriate to suggest that they record only six events in sequence.

EXTENSIONS
- The children can take a copy of page 121 home at the weekend and use it to record significant events on either Saturday or Sunday. This can be followed by a whole-class review of the homework the following week.
- They can use page 121 to describe a day in the life of a favourite fictional character, then swap with a friend who has to identify the character.
- Photocopiable page 119 provides a further opportunity to assess the children's ability to link digital and analogue times.

ON THE BUSES

Whole class
30 minutes

AIM

To calculate time intervals.

WHAT YOU WILL NEED

A bus timetable similar to the one shown below, either drawn on A4 paper and copied for the children or drawn large on the board. You may prefer to change the names of the bus stops to match your own locality.

NB The timetable below does **not** show 24-hour times – see *Developing Shape, Space and Measures with 9–11 year olds* (also by Jon Kurta, published by Scholastic) for work on the 24-hour clock.

	Bus A	Bus B	Bus C
Centre Lane	8.10	8.30	8.45
Express Cinema	8.30		
Shopping Centre	8.55		
Bowling Green	9.10		
High School	9.30		

WHAT TO DO

Ask the children to discuss the route of Bus A with a partner, and to think about how long it takes to travel from each of the locations to the next. When they have had time to discuss this, ask questions (see below) to check their understanding.

Now the children should consider Buses B and C. Explain that these two buses take the same amount of time as Bus A for each step of the journey. The task is to complete the table, filling in the missing times.

During the plenary session, discuss with the children their strategies for completing the table. They may have calculated the time interval for each step of the journey (20, 25, 15 and 20 minutes); or they may have realized that, for example, every time for Bus B is 20 minutes later than the corresponding time for Bus A.

DISCUSSION QUESTIONS

- *Which section of the journey takes the shortest amount of time? Which takes the longest?*
- *How long does it take from Centre Lane to the Shopping Centre? How long from the Express Cinema to the High School?*
- *How did you work out the times for Bus B and Bus C?*

ASSESSMENT

Can the children calculate the times for Buses B and C? Can they explain how they did this? Can they create an accurate timetable for further buses travelling the same route?

EXTENSIONS

- The children can continue the timetable for further buses travelling the same route during the day (they can choose the start times), or construct a timetable for the return journey.
- Another good context for calculating time intervals is TV programme schedules. As with the bus timetables, for this age group it is a good idea to provide a simplified version.

HOW LONG IS A MINUTE?

Whole class, then groups
50 minutes

AIM
To develop a sense of time by estimating short time periods.

WHAT YOU WILL NEED
Stop watches or minute timers (one per group), paper, pencils.

WHAT TO DO
Ask the children to think about how long one minute is:

- *What could you do in one minute?*
- *Is it enough time to walk to the school office and back/run around the perimeter of the playground?*
- *How much writing/how many mental maths questions could you do in one minute?*
- *Could you tell when one minute was over?*

Ask the children to put their heads down on their desks, with their eyes closed. When they think that one minute has passed, they should look up and raise a hand. Note which children underestimate – those who over-estimate will be noticed by everyone else. This warm-up activity can be repeated several times over the course of a fortnight; a possible variation is to have some children 'keeping watch' over the others. When the children have become fairly accurate at estimating the passing of one minute, try 30 seconds or two minutes.

In the main part of the lesson, the children should work in small groups to estimate and then measure the things that they can do in one minute. They should take turns to time each other with a stopwatch. A table (such as the one shown below) can be drawn up for recording results; the class computer may be useful here. Allow enough time for the groups to complete their activities; then bring the class together for discussion and review.

IN ONE MINUTE	Estimate	Actual
Number of times I can write my name		
Number of times I can write the alphabet		
Number of press-ups or sit-ups		
Number of times I can count to 20 in 2s		
Number of pencils I can sharpen		

DISCUSSION QUESTIONS
- *How can you tell when exactly one minute has passed?*
- *What is a good way to estimate how many times you can do something in one minute? [Find out how long it takes to do it two or three times, or how many times you can do it in 15 seconds.]*

ASSESSMENT
How accurately can the children judge the passing of one minute? How sensible are their estimates of what they can do in one minute?

VARIATION
Suggest a series of more extended activities and ask the children to estimate how many minutes each will take to complete. Examples could include: walking the perimeter of the playground, writing out all the times tables (to 10 × 10), tidying their desk, making a model animal from Plasticine, solving a jigsaw puzzle. Emphasize that the purpose of this activity is to estimate as accurately as possible how long each activity will take, then check by timing. The tasks are not meant to be done as quickly as possible.

EXTENSIONS
- The children can use their results as a basis for predictions, answering questions such as: *If you can write your name 8 times in one minute, then how many times can you do it in 5 minutes? How many times in an hour?* Check whether they realize that not all results can be extrapolated in this way: for example, they could not continue doing press-ups at the same rate for an hour. Discuss the suitability of this 'sampling' approach for different predictions.
- Photocopiable page 7.3 provides an opportunity for further discussion of the time that different events take. The children could complete it individually or in pairs, then discuss the questions it raises as a class. The answers are: a) 3 minutes, b) 5 hours, c) 20 minutes, d) 2 hours, e) 1 minute, f) 20 seconds, g) 5 weeks, h) 1 hour.

NAME DATE

TIME

WHICH IS LONGER?

■ In each case, decide which is the longer period of time and explain why.

110 seconds or 2 minutes?	600 minutes or 10 hours?
6 weeks or 40 days?	64 days or 7 weeks?
125 minutes or 2 hours?	4 centuries or 399 years?
3 days or 70 hours?	4 minutes or 250 seconds?
2 years or 800 days?	5 days or 120 hours?

■ Check your answers with a friend.

Did any of the answers surprise you?

SEE 'UNITS OF TIME', PAGE 114.

NAME DATE

MATCHING TIMES

■ For each time given in words, draw hands on the clock face to show the same time. Then draw a line to connect the time in words to the correct digital time.

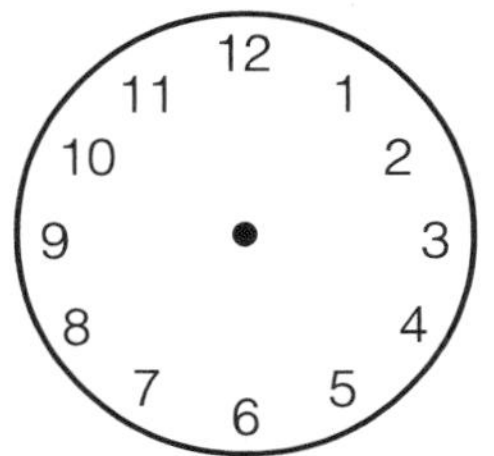	Half past eight	10:15
	A quarter to ten	9:45
	A quarter past ten	8:40
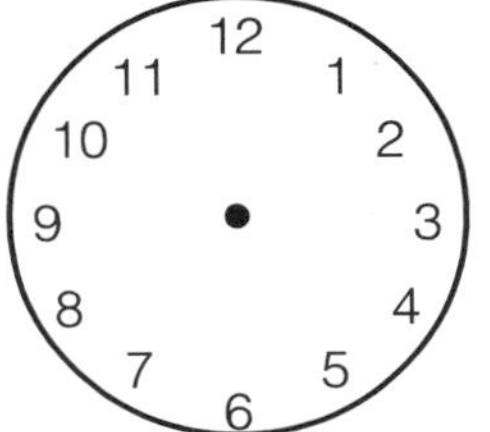	Twenty to nine	6:25
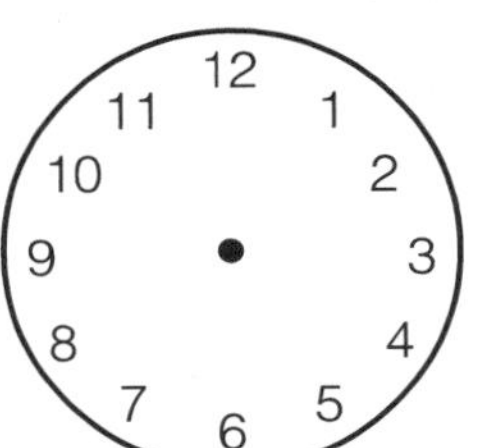	Twenty-five past six	8:30

■ Check your answers with a friend.

Which times are easiest to draw on the clock face? Does your friend agree?

SEE 'A DAY IN THE LIFE', PAGE 115.

TIME

NAME DATE

HOW LONG DOES IT TAKE?

■ Match these time periods to the different events:

5 weeks	3 minutes	5 hours	20 minutes
2 hours	1 minute	20 seconds	1 hour

a) Boiling an egg 	b) Train from London to Glasgow 
c) Teacher reading class a story 	d) Cooking a chicken 
e) Tying shoelaces 	f) Writing my name 
g) Growing cress 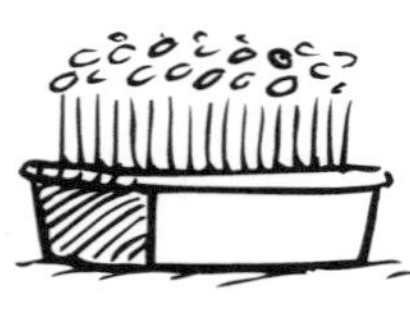	h) A literacy lesson 

■ Do your friends agree?

Use plain paper to write your own 'How long?' quiz.

SEE 'HOW LONG IS A MINUTE?', PAGE 117.

NAME DATE

CLOCK FACES

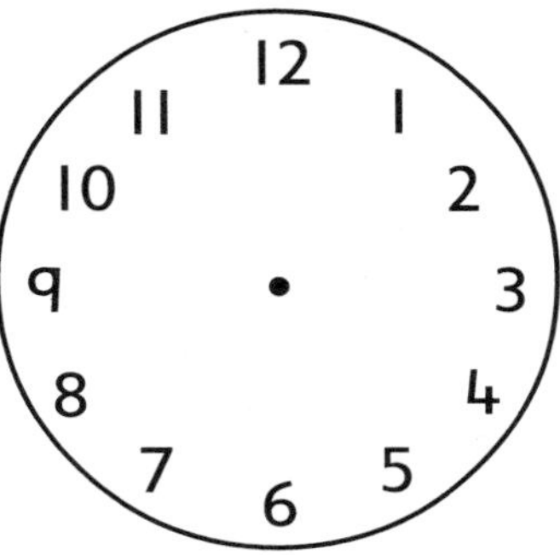

Time I get up

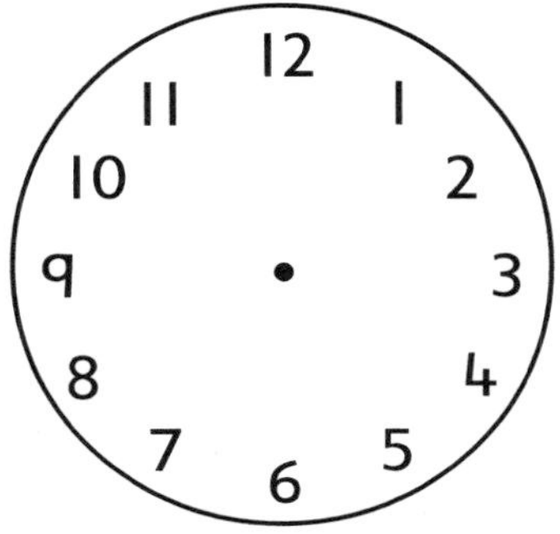

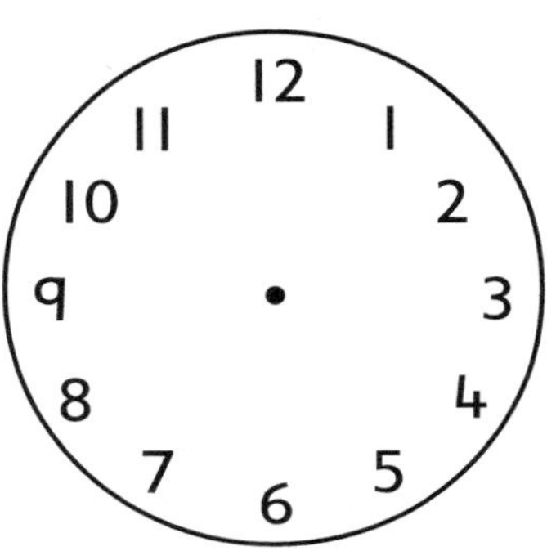

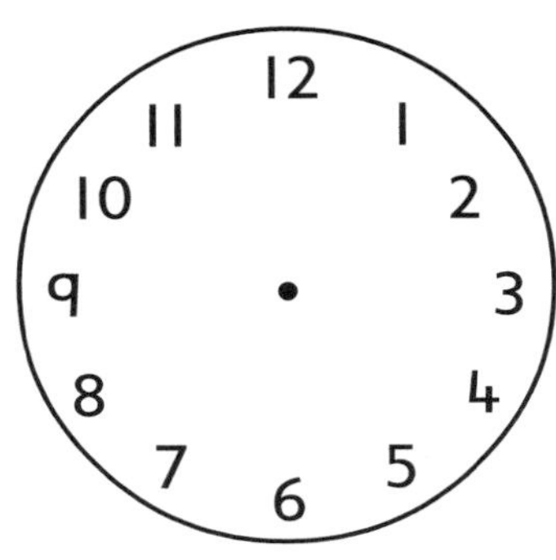

Time I go to bed

SEE 'A DAY IN THE LIFE', PAGE 115.

NAME DATE

CAPITAL LETTERS

A		B		C	
D		E		F	
G		H		I	
J		K		L	
M		N		O	
P		Q		R	
S		T		U	
V		W		X	
Y		Z			

PLEASE REFER TO PAGES 38 AND 39.

NAME DATE

DIFFERENT SHAPES

A

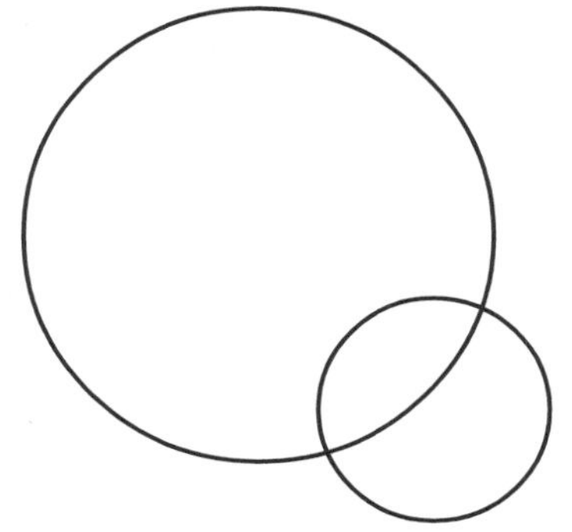

B

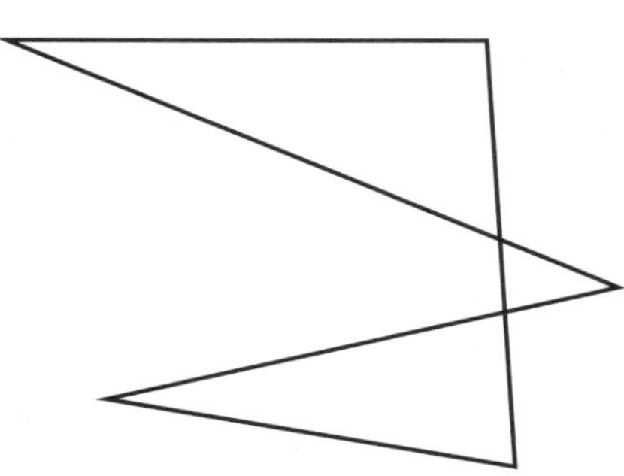

C

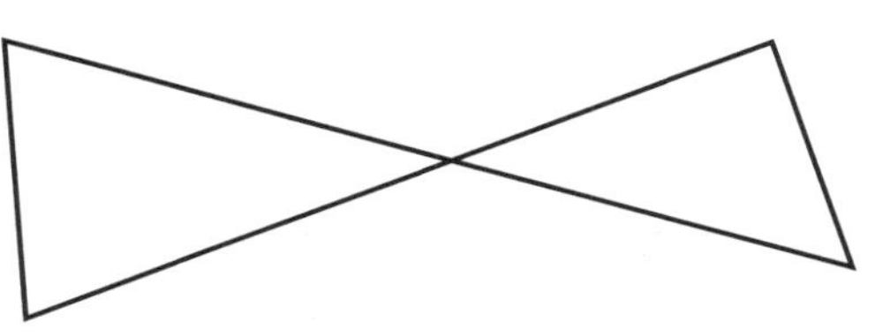

D

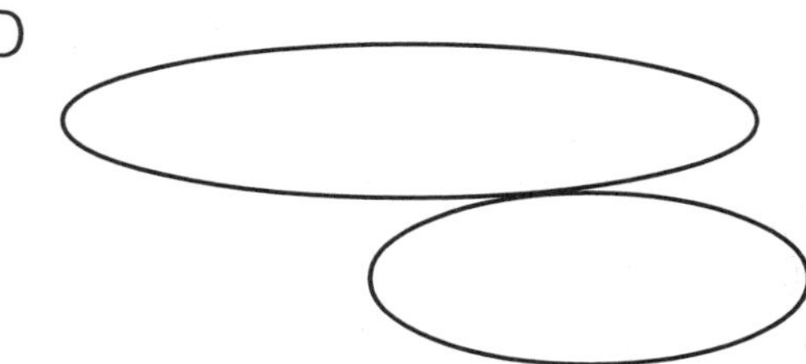

E

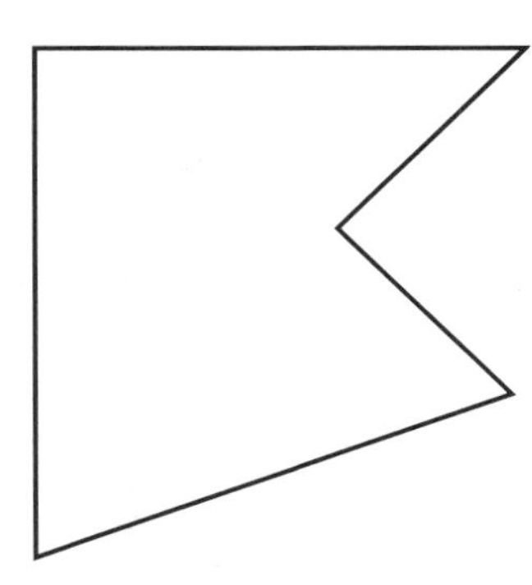

F

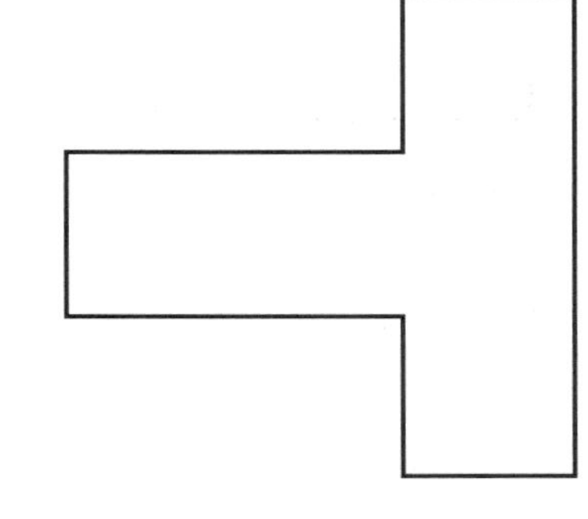

G

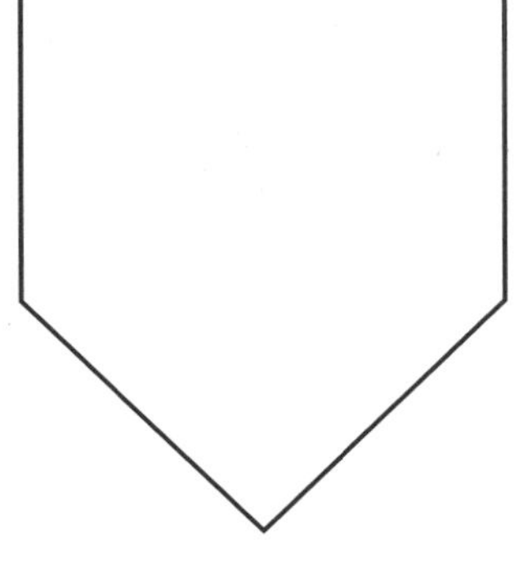

H

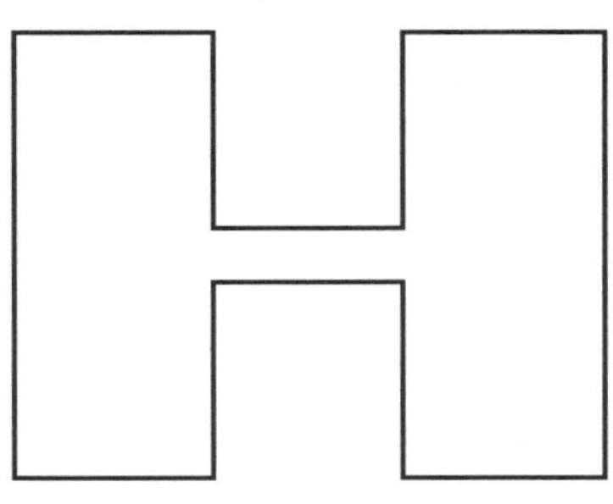

PLEASE REFER TO PAGE 15.

NAME DATE

GEOBOARDS

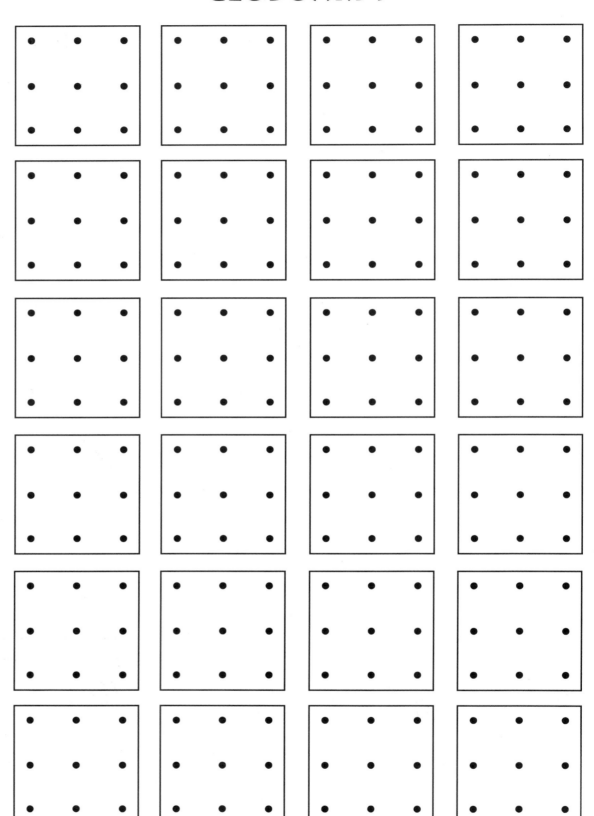

PLEASE REFER TO PAGES 20 AND 85.

NAME DATE

A TANGRAM

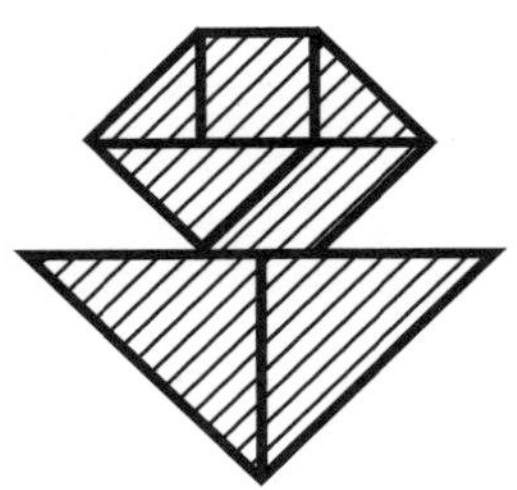
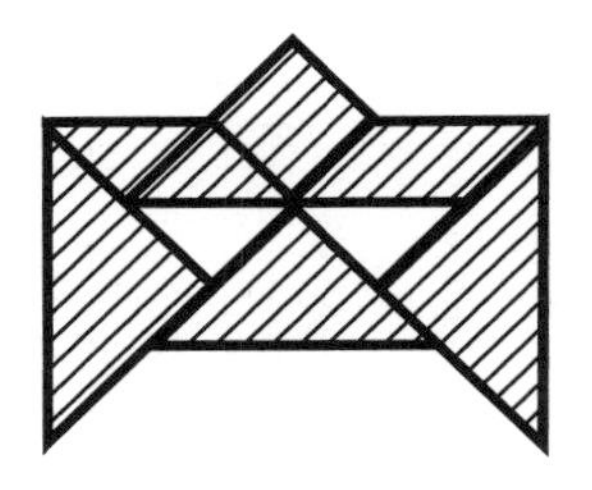
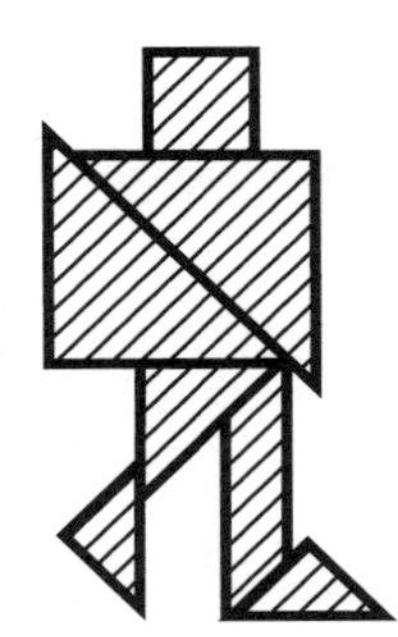
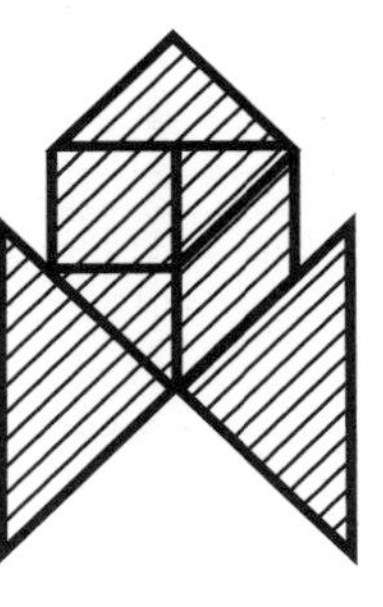
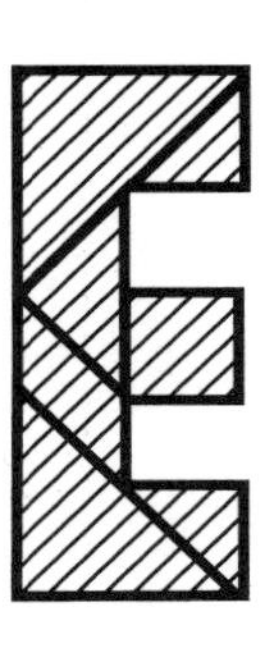

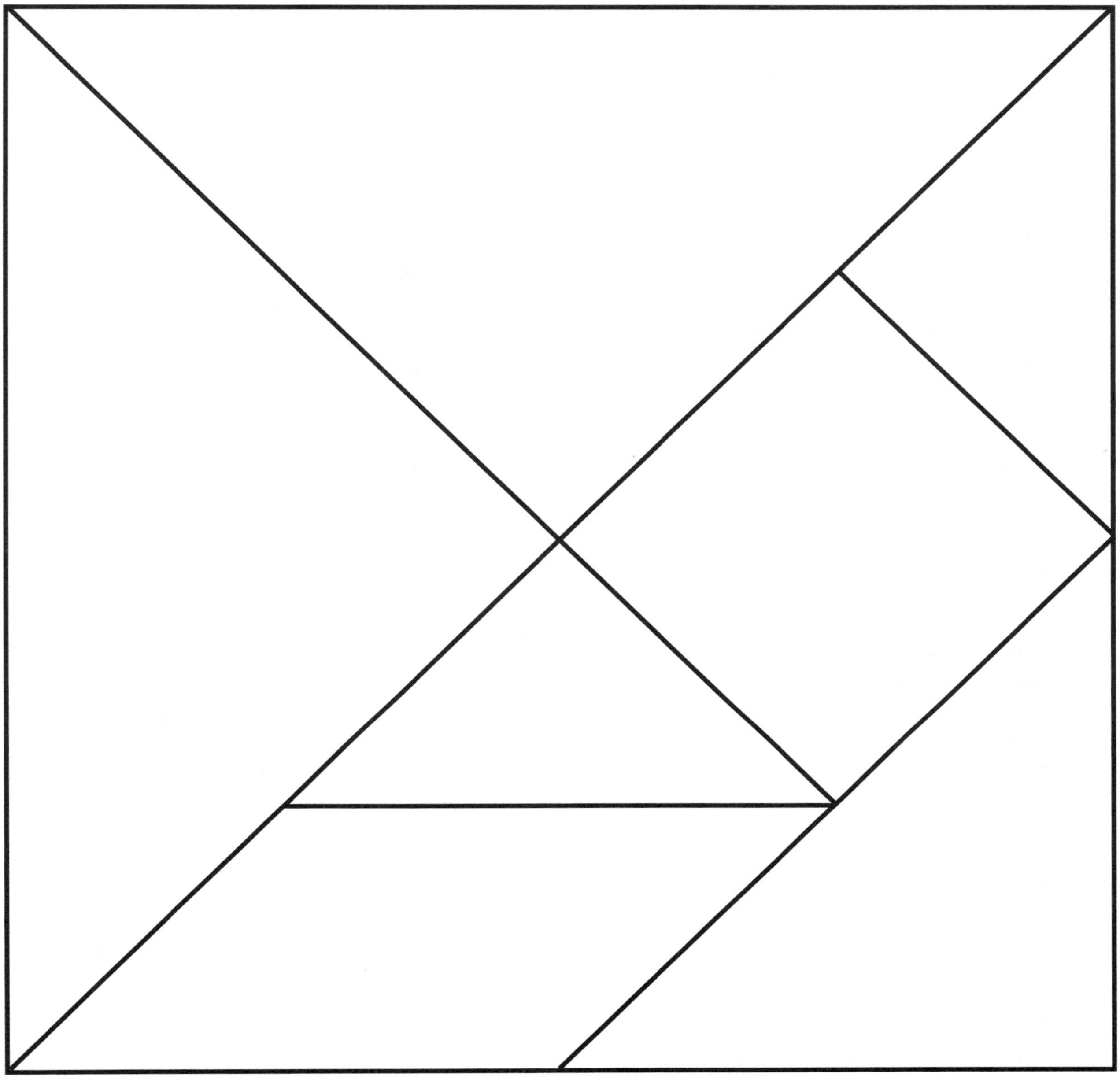

PLEASE REFER TO PAGES 22 AND 53

NAME DATE

MAZES

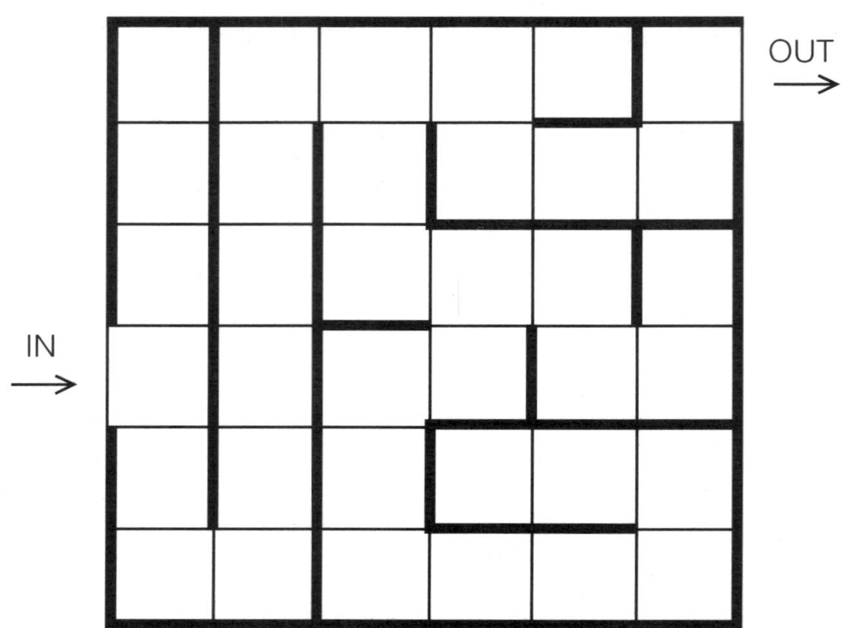

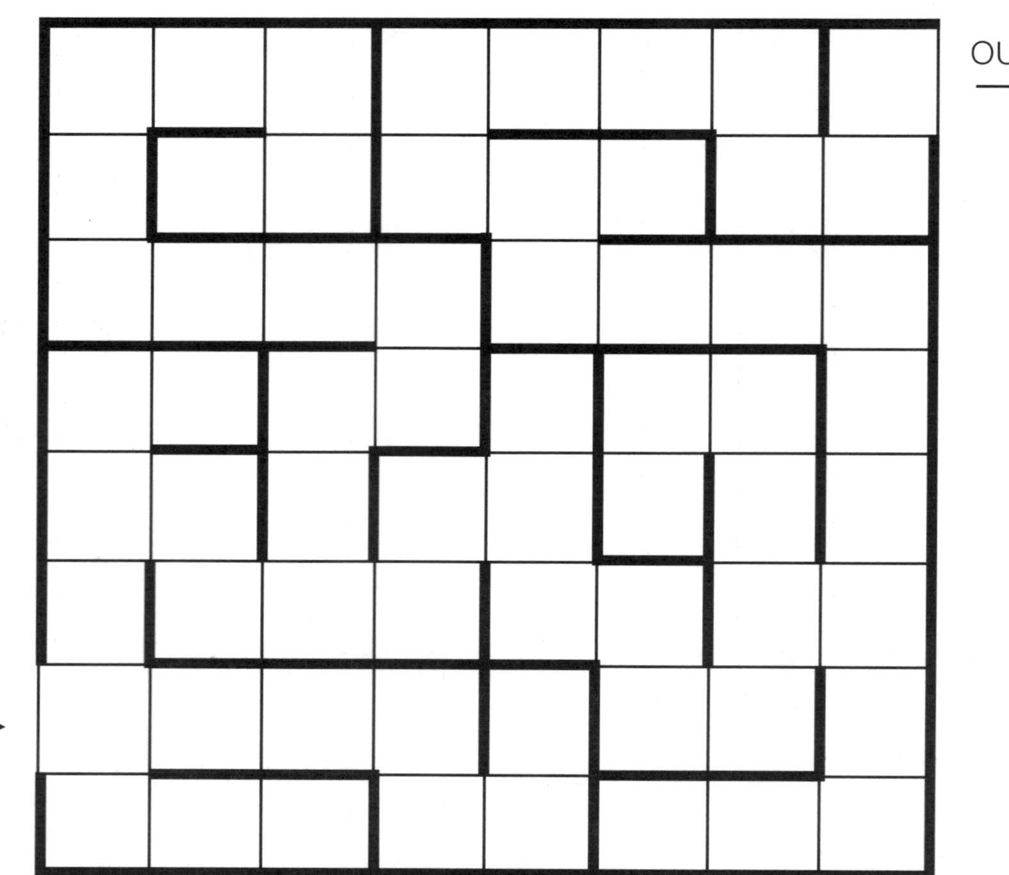

PLEASE REFER TO PAGE 55.

NAME **DATE**

GEOSTRIPS

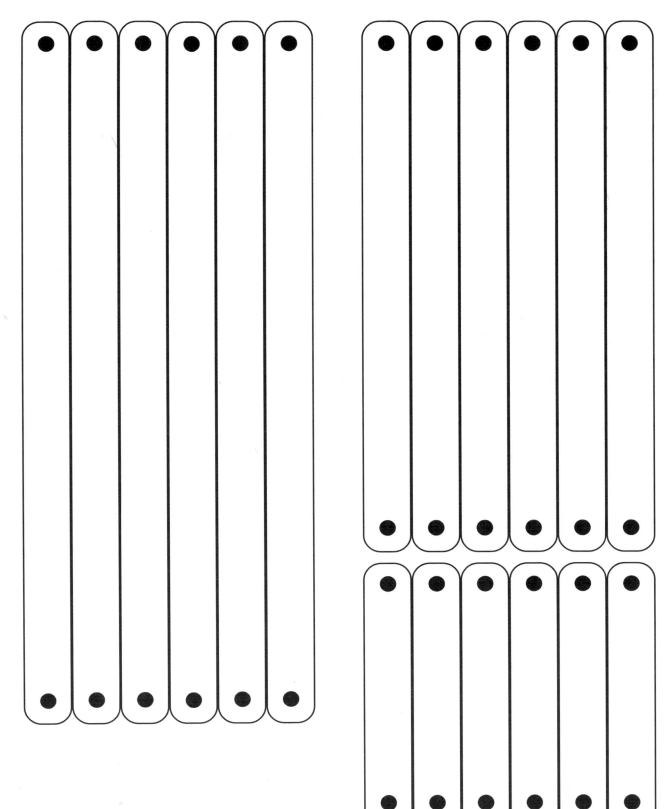

PLEASE REFER TO PAGES 24 AND 65.

PHOTOCOPIABLE

NAME DATE

WRITING FRAME

Today we investigated...

We used...

We found out...

I have learnt that...

Some important maths words I used: